A.J. BRIGNOLE

408-72-7984

BILL SCHRADER

MEMPHIS VALVE & FITTING CO.
P. O. BOX 28836   4310 RALEIGH-LAGRANGE
MEMPHIS, TENNESSEE 38128   901-382-3111

D0463851

Swagelok ®

TUBE FITTING
AND
INSTALLATION MANUAL

By

F. J. Callahan, Jr.
Executive Vice President
Crawford Fitting Company

CRAWFORD FITTING COMPANY
29500 Solon Road
Cleveland, Ohio 44139

PREFACE

SWAGELOK Tube Fittings have attained leadership in the tube connection field because of superior design principles in combination with close manufacturing tolerances and rigid quality control. They have passed the test of time with an unparalleled history of over 25 years of successful on-the-job performance. Proper installation of this precision tube fitting will provide leak tight, trouble-free connections every time.

The illustrated problems and solutions contained within this manual have resulted from extensive field research and laboratory studies conducted by SWAGELOK Research and Development Engineers.

By using this reference manual, you will find solutions to many problems that often occur on the job.

I would like to thank those who have contributed to the preparation of this manual and particularly the many pipe fitters, pipe fitter foremen, instrument engineers and instrument shop personnel whose extensive help, suggestions, contributions and comments made this book possible.

F. J. Callahan, Jr.

Cleveland, Ohio
April, 1974

CONTENTS

GLOSSARY OF TERMS

Definitions of words commonly used in discussing tube fitttings, pipe fittings and their application are included in the "Glossary of Terms".

Absolute zero pressure: The theoretical absence of all pressure, normally expressed as zero pounds per square inch absolute (p.s.i.a.). Absolute pressure units therefore *include* the pressure caused by the weight of the atmosphere at sea level which is 14.7 p.s.i.a.

Absolute zero temperature: The theoretical point at which a substance would have no molecular motion and thus no heat. It is expressed as $-273°C$, $-460°F$, $0°R$ or $0°K$.

AN: Air Force and Navy or Army-Navy.

AND: Air Force-Navy Design.

Annealing: Heating and cooling primarily (a) to induce softness (b) to relieve internal stresses, and (c) to obtain the optimum combination of strength and ductility.

A.S.M.E.: American Society of Mechanical Engineers.

A.S.T.M.: American Society for Testing Materials.

Axial: Along the axis or length of a tube or other cylindrical item.

Axial Movement: Any movement along the axis of the tube.

Bakeout: A method of speeding the outgassing of contaminants in a vacuum system by the use of heat. See Vacuum bakeout.

Brazing: A form of soldering through which two metallic surfaces are joined by melting a silver-copper alloy at about 1200° F.

BTU: British Thermal Unit: The quantity of heat necessary to raise the temperature of one pound of water by 1° F.

Buna: A copolymer compound good for general use as an O-Ring material in oil, water, air with a temperature range of $-65°F$ to $275°F$.

BWR-Boiling Water Reactor: A nuclear reactor that produces steam directly from nuclear fission by boiling water.

Coefficient: A number expressing the ratio of change under certain specified conditions such as temperature, length, volume, etc.

Coefficient of Thermal Expansion: The fractional change in length of a material per degree of temperature change as compared to the length at the reference temperature, usually 0°C (32° F). It is expressed as inch per inch per deg. C or F.

Compressive Force: The squeezing together of material.

Concentricity: The condition of two circles with a common center. In all types of circular seals, the concentricity of the mating members (such as front ferrule and body) is critical to effective sealing.

Corrosion: Eating away or deterioration of a material due to inter-action of two materials. Most familiar example is the rusting of carbon steel.

Creep Strength: The rate of continuous deformation under stress at a specified temperature. Generally expressed as psi to produce 1 per cent elongation in 10,000 hours at an indicated temperature.

Cryogenics: The study, production and utilization of low temperatures.

C_v *(flow co-efficient):* The number of gallons per minute of water that will flow thru a device in the wide open position with a one p.s.i. pressure differential. This is a measurement of valve flow capacity.

Delrin: A thermoplastic acetal resin manufactured by the polymerization of formaldehyde.

DESO: Double end Shut-Off.

Ductility: The property which permits deformation under tension without rupture. Values for "Elongation" and "Reduction of Area" generally are taken as the measure of ductility.

Durometer: An instrument for measuring the hardness of rubber. Measures the resistance of the penetration of an indentor point into the surface of rubber.

Dynamic Seal: A seal required to prevent leakage past parts which are in relative motion.

Elastic Limit: The greatest stress which can be applied to a material (loaded, bent, etc.) below yield and still return to its original size or shape upon removal of the load.

Elastomer: A general term for elastic, rubber-like substances.

Ethylene Propylene Rubber: A synthetic elastomer used for rough service such as steam and hot water to 275°F. EPR has a temperature range of $-65°$ F to $+300°$ F.

Ferrules: Specially designed components used in tube fittings to grip and seal on the outer surface of tubing.

Filler Weld: A weld method which requires the adding of a metal.

Finish: Particular texture or quality of a surface, usually measured by RMS (root mean square) or micro inch.

Flange: Projecting rim, collar, or edge on an object for keeping it in place.

Flexible Tubing: A pliable tube such as an elastomer, a plastic, or a convóluted metal which can return to its original shape after bending.

Flow: Movement of a fluid.

Fluid: A substance having particles which easily move and change their relative position. Both liquids and gases are fluids.

Fluid System: A continuous arrangement of piping or tubing for the transfer of gases or liquids from one location to another. This system can include piping, tubing, valves, gauges, meters, storage tanks, pumps, etc.

Fusion Weld: A weld method in which two metallic parts are joined by heating their surfaces and allowing the metals to flow together.

Gauge pressure: The most common means of expressing system pressure and is measured in pounds per square in. gauge (p.s.i.g.) units. P.S.I.G. units *exclude* the pressure caused by the weight of the atmosphere at sea level. Thus 14.7 p.s.i.a. = 0 p.s.i.g.

Gall: Pickup and tearing of metal caused by high friction and force.

Gas: A fluid which tends to expand without limit.

Hardness: Resistance to plastic deformation by indentation, penetration, scratching or bending. Expressed by means of "Brinell," "Rockwell," "Scleroscope" or "Vickers" Hardness Numbers depending upon the testing machine used.

Heat Sink: A method used to dissipate heat.

Hydrogen Embrittlement: Embrittlement caused by entrance of hydrogen into a metal.

HTGCR: High Temperature Gas Cooled Reactor.

I.S.O. International Standards Organization.

I.D.: Abbreviation for inside diameter.

J. I. C.: Joint Industry Conference.

Kel-F: A thermoplastic polymer with excellent chemical inertness and a temperature range of $-320°F$ to $+300°F$.

Leak Rate: Flow of a fluid volume per unit of time at a differential pressure.

Lift To Seal: A mechanical action by which leak-tight seals are effected without torque, as in a SWAGELOK Tube Fitting.

Liquid: A fluid that has definite volume, no definite form, is not solid and can readily flow.

LMFBR: Liquid Metal Fast Breeder Reactor. A nuclear reactor that produces more nuclear fuel than it burns up.

LNG: Liquified Natural Gas: A process by which gas is manufactured and stored at cryogenic temperatures.

Load Train: Combination of fitting components that generate the seal force (mechanical drive train).

Metal To Glass Transition: A means of joining metal to glass. CAJON Company utilizes a one-step "Housekeeper Seal" to accomplish this.

Mirror Finish: A bright, polished surface.

M.C.F.H.: Micron Cubic Feet per Hour — a leak rate.

Micro-Inch: Average deviation from the mean surface or roughness height. (Millionth of an inch — 0.000001″).

M.I.G. (Metal Inert Gas): A form of welding used to weld non-ferrous metals such as aluminum. An electric arc is struck between a continuous filler consumable electrode and the work to form a weld.

A shielding gas, most often Argon, is used to shield the arc from impurities in the atmosphere.

MIL: Military Specification.

M.S.:   Military Standard or Military Specification.

Neoprene Rubber: A chloroprene polymer and one of the earliest American synthetic rubbers. Under some low temperature conditions, they may temporarily crystallize, lose the O-Ring shape and leak.

Nylon: A thermoplastic polymer of an extremely tough nature and effective resistance to chemical attack.

O.D.:   Abbreviation for outside diameter.

O.F.H.C.:   (Oxygen Free High Conductivity):   Copper which is free of oxygen, Copper Oxide, and residual Copper Deoxidants. It is commercially pure with high electrical conductance and a high resistance to hydrogen embrittlement.

Outgassing: Used in vacuum terminology, the vaporization of contaminants within a vacuum system as pressure is decreased.

Plastic Range: The stress range where the material will take on permanent deformation due to some load above yield.

Pressure: The force distributed upon a surface, usually expressed in pounds per square inch (p.s.i.).

Burst Pressure: The pressure at which rupture takes place.

Pressure Drop: A decrease in pressure along the direction of flow caused by friction and other losses associated with flow in a fluid system.

Working Pressure: A pressure below yield pressure and burst pressure at which it is considered safe to use tubing or other fluid system components.

Yield Pressure: The pressure at which the yield point of material is reached. The yield point of the tubing has been reached when the tubing swells or stretches and does not return to its original size after the pressure has been removed.

PWR: Pressurized Water Reactor. A nuclear reactor that produces steam indirectly from nuclear fission by heating water under pressure.

Pyrex: A composition of glass ceramics.

Quad Toroid: The four segments of a torus in a CAJON Vacuum Flange which contain the sealing gasket.

Radial Movement: The expansion or contraction of the tube diameter.

Residual Spring: The condition where the sealing member (such as a front ferrule) is always in a sprung condition. This greatly aids in thermal cycling and make/break sealing ability.

R.M.S.: (Root Mean Square) The measure of surface roughness obtained as the square root of the sum of the squares of micro-inch deviation from true flat.

Rotary: Turning on an axis; pertaining to rotation.

S.A.E.: Society of Automotive Engineers, Inc.

S.C.F.H.: Standard Cubic Feet per Hour.

S.C.F.M.: Standard Cubic Feet per Minute.

Seal: Any device used to prevent the passage of a gas or liquid.

Seal Force: The force that presses sealing members together.

Silicone Rubber: A group of synthetic elastomers with excellent low temperature flexibility. Some to −100°F and on the other range to 450°F.

SNG: Synthetic Natural Gas. The process of gassification of light liquid hydrocarbons.

Soldering: A metal joining process performed at +400° to +500°F. by melting a tin-lead alloy.

Static Seal: Seal designed to work between parts having no relative motion.

Strain: The movement of material within a fixed length of dimension. That is, inches per inch.

Stress: The amount of load placed on material, usually expressed in pounds per square inch.

Swage: A term meaning to cold work (permanently deform) a piece of metal.

SWAGELOK Tube Fitting: A patented, precision machined, quality tube fitting employing two ferrules which swage the tubing to obtain the ultimate in a reliable, leaktight Tube Fitting connection.

Tee: A fitting in the shape of a "T" with three connections.

Run of a Tee: The straight section of a Tee that has a connection on each end.

Branch of a Tee: The section of a Tee that is at a right angle to the run and having one connection.

Tensile Force: A force exerted to stretch or tend to pull apart a material.

Tensile Strength: The tensile strength of a material is the highest stress that a material can withstand before failure or rupture occurs.

TFE: A tetrafluoroethylene polymer with excellent chemical resistance and a self-lubricating quality. Temperatures up to 450°F.

Thrust: This is the force trying to push the tube out of the fitting. It results from system pressure against the exposed tube area. Example: If a system has 100 psi working against one square inch of area, the thrust is equal to 100 lbs.

T.I.G.: (Tungsten Insert Gas): A form of welding used to weld "hard-to-weld" metals. Intense heat of an electric arc is struck between a non-consumable tungsten electrode and the metal to be welded. A shielding gas, most often Argon, is used to shield the arc from impurities in the atmosphere.

Torque: A force that produces or tends to produce rotary motion.

Torus: A surface generated by the revolution of a circle about an axis lying in its plane. Example: O-Ring.

Tube Fitting: A device which is used with tubing for connections in a fluid system.

Tubing: Tubing is metal, glass or plastic in hollow, cylindrical form. Metal tubing, for gas and liquid applications, should have sufficient ductility to be bent into desired shapes.

Annealed Tubing: Annealed tubing is soft enough to allow proper bending for fluid system installations.

Fractional Tubing: Most metal and plastic tubing, in the United States and Canada, is fractional tubing that is sized according to the outside diameter in even fractions of an inch; 1/16″, 1/8″, 3/16″, 1/4″, etc. The foreign market, however, uses mostly millimeter sized tubing and so have many of the United States and Canadian markets particularly in the use of glass tubing. SWAGELOK Tube Fittings are available in both fractional and millimeter sizes.

Hydraulic Tubing: Hydraulic tubing is annealed tubing that is intended for use in fluid systems.

Mechanical Tubing: This tubing is for fabricating parts such as racks, scaffolding, etc. It should not be used in fluid work.

Pressure tubing: Same as hydraulic tubing.

Tube Wall: Tube wall or tube wall thickness is the O.D. minus the I.D. divided by 2. It is often abbreviated as "t". The Tube Wall formula is: $t = \dfrac{OD - ID}{2}$

Ultimate Strength: Same as tensile strength.

Vacuum: The absence or partial absence of the standard pressure exerted by the atmosphere. It is oftened expressed in the following units:

1.) inches of mercury (in. Hg.)
2.) millimeters of mercury (mm Hg.)
3.) torr
4.) p.s.i.a
5.) microns

Vacuum bake-out: The addition of heat to a vacuum system to promote vaporization of contaminants and reduce pump-down time.

Vacuum rating: Expressed in units of vacuum given above.

NOTE: It is *not* a leak rating.

Viscosity: A manifestation of internal friction opposed to mobility. The property of fluids and plastic solids by which they resist an instantaneous change to shape, i. e., resistance to flow.

Viton: A fluorocarbon rubber used as an O-Ring material. Especially good for hard vacuum service and a temperature range of −40° to 450° F.

Welding: The strongest permanent metal joining process which is performed at a temperature near 3000° F.

Yield Point: The yield point of a material is defined as the stress at which elongation takes place with little or no increase in applied force. Once a material has gone beyond the yield point, permanent deformation takes place and it will not return to its original dimensions when the force is removed.

Patented

CHAPTER I

USING *SWAGELOK* TUBE FITTINGS

SWAGELOK TUBE FITTING INSTALLATION

SWAGELOK Tube Fittings are easy to install. There is only one design of SWAGELOK Tube Fittings regardless of material, size, pressure or application. Therefore, there is only one set of instructions for connecting a SWAGELOK Tube Fitting.

INSTALLATION INSTRUCTIONS

SWAGELOK Tube Fittings come to you completely assembled, finger-tight. They are ready for immediate use. Disassembly before use can result in dirt or foreign material getting into the fitting and causing leaks. SWAGELOK Tube Fittiings are installed in three easy steps as shown in Fig. 1, 2, and 3.

Fig. 1

Step. 1. Simply insert the tubing into the SWAGELOK Tube Fitting. Make sure that the tubing rests firmly on the shoulder of the fitting and that the nut is finger-tight.

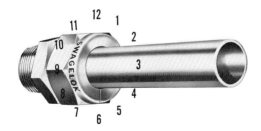

Fig. 2

Step 2. Before tightening the SWAGELOK nut, scribe the nut at the 6:00 o'clock position.

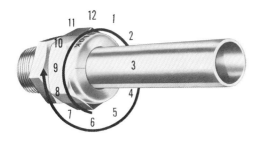

Fig. 3

Step 3. Now, while holding the fitting body steady with a backup wrench or vise, tighten the nut one-and-one-quarter turns.* Watching the scribe mark, make one complete revolution and continue to the 9:00 o'clock position.

By using the scribe mark, there will be no doubt in your mind that the fitting has been tightened one-and-one-quarter turns* required for a proper installation. This gives you a torque-free, leakproof seal. The only tools you need are two wrenches.

HIGH PRESSURE APPLICATION

Due to the variation of tubing diameters, a common starting point is desirable. Therefore, with a wrench, snug up the nut until the tubing will not turn by hand in the fitting or move axially. At this point, scratch or mark the nut of the fitting. Using the scribe or mark on the nut to keep track of the turns, tighten the nut one-and-one-quarter turns while holding the body stationary with a backup wrench. The fitting is now ready to hold vacuum or pressures high enough to burst the tubing.

NO DISASSEMBLY INSPECTION

Having made the tube connection, there is no need to disassemble a SWAGELOK Fitting to inspect the connection after assembly. Exhaustive tests and on-the-job performance have proven that disassembly is not needed as long as the fitting has been pulled up in accordance with the installation instructions.

*For 1/16" 1/8" and 3/16" size tube fittings, only 3/4 turn from finger-tight is necessary.

RE-TIGHTENING INSTRUCTIONS

SWAGELOK Fittings can be disconnected and re-tightened repeatedly and a leak-tight connection results every time. The instructions for re-tightening are graphically shown in Figs. 4, 5 and 6.

Fig. 4
Fitting shown in disconnected position.

Fig. 5
Tubing with pre-swaged ferrules inserted into the fitting until front ferrule sits in fitting and the tubing is bottomed against the shoulder of the body.

Fig. 6
Tighten nut by hand. Rotate nut about one quarter turn with wrench (or to original position) then snug slightly with wrench.

PRE-SWAGING AND HYDRAULIC SWAGING

When SWAGELOK Tube Fittings are to be installed in cramped quarters or overhead where ladders must be used, it is sometimes found advantageous to use a pre-swaging tool or to pull up a fitting on the tubing in an open ground area, thus pre-swaging the ferrules. The pre-swaging tool or the tube fitting body is then removed and the tubing with nut and pre-swaged ferrules can now be attached to a fitting merely by following the re-tightening instructions.

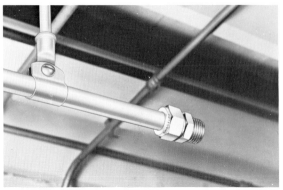

Fig. 7

Tubing 20 feet above ground (with union connected) to which it is desired to connect a run of tubing.

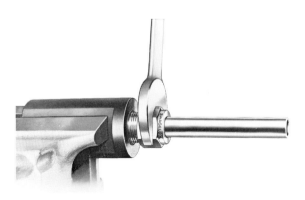

Fig. 8

At ground level, a SWAGELOK pre-swaging tool is used to swage ferrules on to the tubing, to be installed by pulling the nut up in accordance with installation instructions.

Fig. 9

The nut is loosened and the tubing with pre-swaged ferrules is removed from the pre-swaging tool.

Fig. 10

The connection can now be made by merely snugging up the nut as given in the re-tightening instructions.

Fig. 11
Completed Installation.

SWAGELOK HYDRAULIC SWAGING UNIT

Hydraulic swaging is suggested for larger size tube fittings (1¼"
and up).

| Fig. 12 | Fig. 13 |

The SWAGELOK Hydraulic Swaging Unit is designed to make a
safe and reliable torque-free, leak-proof seal on large tubing sizes.

The Hydraulic Swaging Unit consists of a Swaging Tool and an
Accessory Case. The Accessory Case contains a Hydraulic Pump, Hose
and Service Equipment.

Part Number	For
HSU-2000	1¼" SWAGELOK Fittings
HSU-2400	1½" SWAGELOK Fittings
HSU-3200	2" SWAGELOK Fittings

NOTE: SWAGELOK Carbon Steel Fittings are designed for use
with high quality Soft Annealed Carbon Steel Tubing ASTM A-179
or equivalent; SWAGELOK Stainless Steel Fittings are designed for
use with high quality Soft Annealed Stainless Steel Tubing ASTM
A-269 or equivalent.

Tubing O.D.(")	RECOMMENDED WALL THICKNESS		
	Material	Min. Wall	Max. Wall
1¼	Carbon Steel	.065	.180
1¼	Stainless Steel	.065	.156
1½	Carbon Steel	.083	.220
1½	Stainless Steel	.083	.188
2	Carbon Steel	.095	.220
2	Stainless Steel	.095	.188

HERE'S HOW THE *SWAGELOK* FITTING FUNCTIONS

SWAGELOK Tube fittings provide a leak-proof, torque-free seal at all tubing connections and eliminate costly, hazardous leaks in instrumentation and process tubing.

In the illustration, notice that the tubing is supported ahead of the ferrules by the fitting body. Two ferrules grasp tightly around the tube with no damage to the tube wall. There is virtually no constriction of the inner wall insuring minimum flow restriction. Exhaustive tests have proven that the tubing will yield before a SWAGELOK Tube Fitting will leak.

The secret of the SWAGELOK Tube Fitting is that all the action in the fitting moves along the tube axially instead of with a rotary motion. Since no torque is transmitted from the fitting to the tubing, there is no initial strain which might weaken the tubing.

The SWAGELOK patented sequential swaging action overcomes variations in tube materials, wall thickness and hardness by its double ferrule inter-action. Ferrule inter-action thus overcomes most of the variables which cause other fittings to fail.

SWAGELOK Tube Fittings are easily installed with no special tools. See the installation instructions on pages 9 & 10.

CHECKLIST FOR EXCELLENCE IN TUBE FITTINGS

DESIGN

A Tube Fitting Should . . .
- **Be self-aligning.**
- Work on **thick or thin** wall tubing.
- Have **tube support** ahead of the seal to resist vibration.
- Work on **any tube** material.
- Have all components made of the **same material** as the fitting body for thermal compatibility and corrosion resistance.
- Have a **residual spring** condition so that temperature cycling will not cause leakage.
- Seal on **machined surfaces.**
- Seal between ferrule and body at a point **different from where the heavy work** is performed.
- **Compensate** for the normal variables encountered in tubing materials.
- **Not** create torque or leave a **residual strain** on the tubing.
- **Not weaken** the tube wall.
- **Not** significantly **reduce** flow area.

PERFORMANCE

A Tube Fitting Should . . .
- Contain any pressure up to the burst point of the tubing **without leakage.**
- Work on **vacuum** as well as **low** or **high** pressures.
- Seal **consistently at cryogenic** temperatures.
- Seal **consistently at elevated** temperatures up to the maximum tubing temperature rating.
- Seal **consistently over a wide range** of temperature cycling.
- Seal repeatedly under **make-and-break** conditions.

ASSEMBLY

A Tube Fitting Should . . .
- Use **geometry rather than torque** for uniformity of make-up (1¼ turns).
- **Not** require **disassembly and inspection** before or after initial make-up.
- **Not require special tools** for assembly.

SERVICE

A Tube Fitting Should . . .
- Be **readily available** in all sizes, materials, end connections and configurations from local distributor stocks, with substantial back-up stocks to support distributor inventories.
- Be designed, manufactured, sold, and serviced by experienced **tube fitting specialists** who understand and respect the need for reliable performance.

TOOLS

To connect SWAGELOK Tube Fittings to tubing, the only tools needed are standard wrenches. Adjustable wrenches should be of good quality and adjusted so that there is no play on the nut or body hex. If poor wrenches are used, or if they are adjusted improperly, there is danger of slipping off the fitting or nut (see Fig. 14). Poor wrenches or improperly adjusted wrenches will damage and distort nuts, often ruin the fitting and, if they slip off, can result in injury.

Fig. 14
Poor wrench used improperly. Notice contact only on corners of nut due to loose fit of improperly adjusted wrench.

Fig. 15
Damage to nut caused by use of improper wrenches.

For construction work or installation jobs where the same size fitting predominates, open-end wrenches are recommended for reliable wrench performance and minimum installation time (see Fig. 16). Do not try to save money by using cheap or worn wrenches. The investment in good wrenches will provide more efficient installations and prevent injury to the worker. The fitting body should always be held stationary with a backup wrench or bench vise, and the fitting nut turned to accomplish the connection or re-tightening (see Fig. 17). Do not turn the body while holding the nut stationary.

Fig. 16
Open end wrench on hex. Proper wrench will provide efficient installation.
Notice full contact on flats of nut hex when proper wrench is used.

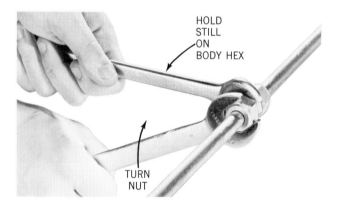

HOLD
STILL
ON
BODY HEX

TURN
NUT

Fig. 17

The size of open-end wrenches and adjustable wrenches required for tube fitting installation, is best determined by checking the dimensions in the SWAGELOK catalog. When using a combination of open-end and adjustable wrenches, it is good practice to use the adjustable wrench on the fitting body. This will minimize the possibility of distorting the tube fitting nut.

When possible, connect to the branch of a tee in a bench vise. For field connection, a pipe wrench can be used on the wrench pad of the tee to hold the tee steady while connecting the tubing to the branch (see Fig. 18).

SWAGELOK TEE WRENCH

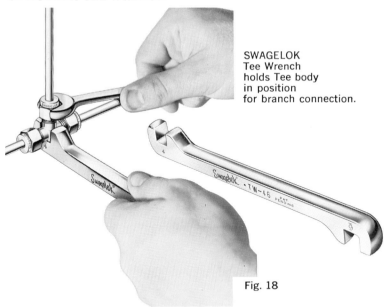

SWAGELOK
Tee Wrench
holds Tee body
in position
for branch connection.

Fig. 18

The SWAGELOK Tee Wrench is a unique wrench designed to eliminate strain on the tubing and simplify installation of tees.

In general practice, some type of adjustable wrench is used to hold the body of the tee. This type of wrench can be awkward to handle and can also damage the body of the tee or the fitting connection.

The Tee Wrench, designed to hold ⅜″ and ¼″ SWAGELOK Tee bodies, is made of chrome-plated, hardened tool steel. The wrench is extremely durable, compact and convenient to use.

Use of the SWAGELOK Tee Wrench on the job will speed up installation, avoid damage to the tee body and will eliminate any torque or twisting of the tubing that could cause an improper connection.

SWAGELOK RATCHET WRENCH

For easier and faster connection work on copper or aluminum tubing, SWAGELOK Ratchet Wrenches can be employed. These wrenches can be used anywhere but are especially designed for use on tube fittings located in places where the degree of swing is limited. The SWAGELOK Ratchet Wrench can be slipped over the tube and then dropped over the nut. By using a smaller opening, equal to the tube diameter, it is possible to have the wrench engage five corners of the nut hex (see Fig. 19). This allows the ratchet wrench to automatically equalize torque over five corners of the hexagon nut, preventing distortion, increasing strength, and insuring grip. Due to the higher torques involved in steel and stainless steel tubing, these wrenches are not recommended for such tubing.

Fig. 19
Ratchet wrench engages (5) corners of nut.

Fig. 20
Open-end wrench bears only on two sides.

THREAD GALLING

In producing a swage in tubing, the threads of the fittings give considerable mechanical advantage so that little force is needed to turn the wrench and make up the fitting. The forces on these threads, however, are very high and, in certain materials, such as 316 stainless steel, Inconel, Monel and other special alloys, thread pickup or galling can result.

Galling is prevented in the tube end of SWAGELOK Fittings by special nut treatments applied during manufacturing. Galling is a problem with pipe threads where interference conditions are part of the design (see Fig. 21).

Galled Pipe Thread

Fig. 21

In order to prevent this galling of pipe threads, Crawford Fitting Company developed a thread lubricant and anti-gall family of lubricants called "GOOP". There are four types of GOOP: Silver GOOP; Blue GOOP; High Purity GOOP and Vac GOOP. The use of TFE Tape, called "Strip-Teeze" has gained wide acceptance in recent years (see Figs. 22 - 23).

Fig. 22

SILVER GOOP®

Silver GOOP is formulated as an antiseize compound for threaded parts of stainless steel and super alloys. (Silver GOOP is not recommended for aluminum or magnesium.) When subjected to temperatures up to 1500° F., non-melting Silver GOOP stays in place. It does not drip off red hot surfaces, nor give off poisonous metal or oxide fumes at high temperatures. Silver GOOP's balanced composition keeps it between mating surfaces to prevent seizing, regardless of force applied. It lowers take-up torque on threaded parts, nuts, bolts and pipe threads. Silver GOOP resists water washout, forming a bond with the surface to which it is applied. A new application of GOOP should be used every time a joint is taken apart and re-tightened. Silver GOOP is available in tubes (1 oz.) and cans (1 lb.).

BLUE GOOP®

Blue GOOP is an antiseizing anti-galling compound for use on titanium, stainless steel, magnesium and high temperature alloys. It is impervious to water washout, acids, and all petroleum solvents. It can be used to 400° F. It will not drip, run or lose lubricity under severe conditions. Blue GOOP is available in tubes (2 oz.) and cans, (1 lb.).

HIGH PURITY GOOP®

High Purity GOOP is an antiseizing compound for use on titanium, stainless steel, aluminum and high temperature alloys. It is inert in conditions up to 400° F. It can be used when oily contamination may otherwise be a problem. It is non-corrosive to metals, impervious to moisture, high voltage and thermal cycling. High Purity GOOP is available in 1 oz. tubes.

VAC GOOP®

VAC GOOP is an anti-gall sealant formulated for vacuum systems. The low vapor pressure of VAC GOOP minimizes outgassing problems. The inert ingredients of VAC GOOP assure compatibility with all materials used in a system. VAC GOOP is available in tubes (1 oz.). Can be used up to 200°C.

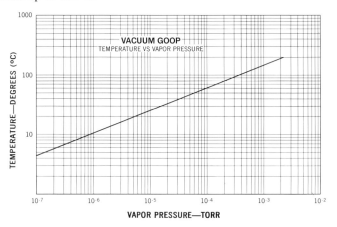

STRIP TEEZE® TAPE

576" x ¼" ROLL
288" x ½" ROLL

Fig. 23

Recommend For:
Chemicals • Corrosives • Hydraulic Fluids • Freon 22 • Aromatic Fuels • Plastics • Aluminum • Stainless Steel • Ceramic • Synthetic Rubber • Monel and Carbon Steel Pipe
  Temperatures: −250°F to +450°F.

HOW STRIP TEEZE TAPE IS APPLIED

Lay end of tape beginning with second thread from the end, and hold in place with thumb. Wrap in direction of thread clockwise for right hand thread, counter clockwise for left hand thread. Draw free end around threads tauntly, so that it conforms to threaded surface. Press in firmly at overlap point. Tape will hold in position by itself.

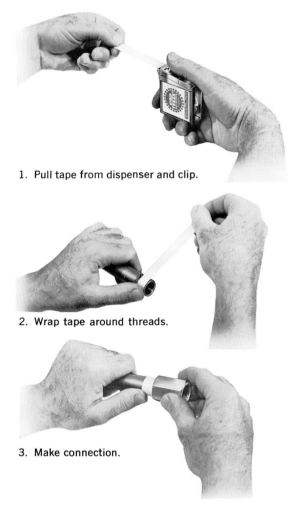

1. Pull tape from dispenser and clip.

2. Wrap tape around threads.

3. Make connection.

Fig. 24

CLIPPER-DISPENSER

The handy clipper-dispenser is precision made to fit and operate on the top of the clear plastic box in which Strip Teeze is packaged.

The tape is clipped off by depressing the top assembly with the thumb. To obtain another length of tape, rotate knurled wheel with thumb, in direction shown by arrow in illustration, just enough to dispense tape. Grasp tape with fingers, and pull tape to desired length, and clip.

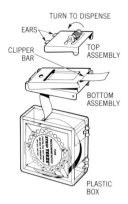

Fig. 25

CHAPTER II

TUBING

ADVANTAGES OF TUBING

Tubing can effect considerable cost savings over pipe in connecting components of fluid systems. The advantages of using tubing for such connections are:

1. *Ease of Installation:* Only standard wrenches are needed to install SWAGELOK Tube Fittings. No threading, flaring, soldering or welding is required. (see Fig. 26).

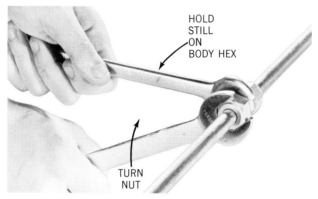

HOLD
STILL
ON
BODY HEX

TURN
NUT

Fig. 26

2. *Better Strength to Weight Ratio:* Full wall thickness of tubing is used in containing pressure since no threading is necessary. Threading reduces effective wall thickness in pipe. (see Fig. 27). The resultant lighter weight of tubing makes tubing less expensive to transport, easier to assemble, require less support, and occupy less space.

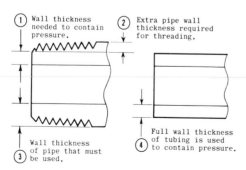

① Wall thickness needed to contain pressure.

② Extra pipe wall thickness required for threading.

③ Wall thickness of pipe that must be used.

④ Full wall thickness of tubing is used to contain pressure.

Fig. 27

3. *Lower Pressure Drop:* Sharp bends and discontinuities of piping systems are not present in the gradual bends and smooth inside diameter of a tubed system (see Fig. 28).

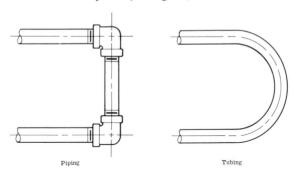

Piping   Tubing

Fig. 28

Fig. 29
Typical application showing use of tubing. (photo courtesy Southwest Industries)
(2) Threaded Joints
(2) Separate Fittings

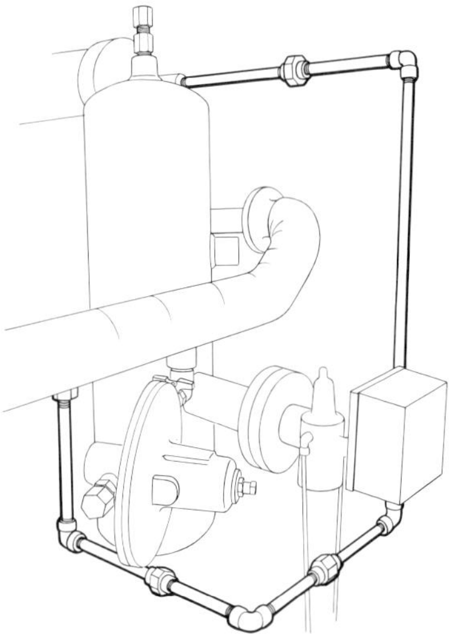

Fig. 30
Schematic of similar type of application showing the number of connections necessary if piping were used.
(16) Threaded Joints
(7) Separate Fittings

4. *Fewer Connections Needed:* Bending of tubing substitutes for many pipe fittings. Tubing is very adaptable and can be bent around many obstructions (see Figs. 29 and 32).

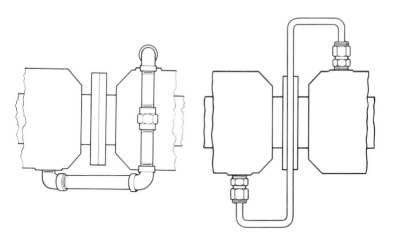

Fig. 31
Pipe Fittings used to Connect
Jacketed Pipe.
(10 potential leaks)

Fig. 32
Tube Fittings required for same
Installation.
(4 potential leaks)

5. *Leak Tight:* At high pressures, pipe connections can leak! Tubing systems connected with SWAGELOK Tube Fittings are leak-tight without using sealing compounds. Compressed air, steam, hydrogen, helium, or hydraulic oil are very expensive services in a plant or refinery. A cheap fitting that leaks costs more money than a SWAGELOK Tube Fitting that provides positive performance.

6. *Easy Maintenance.* Every SWAGELOK Tube Fitting acts as a union. When disassembly is necessary, it is simple. This, coupled with leak-tightness, means easy maintenance. There is no need to disconnect a series of pipe lengths and fittings to remove a particular component from the system.

TUBING MATERIALS

In the Selection of Materials: The operating environment requires certain material properties in order to obtain reasonable life and satisfactory performance. The characteristics of the tubing material, the conditions of corrosion, temperature and stress, (plus sound engineering judgment) determine the material properties required.

Tubing is available in many materials including:

METAL

Aluminum	Nickel	Tantalum
Copper	Carpenter 20	Titanium
Hastelloys	Stainless Steel	Zircaloy
Inconel	Steel (Carbon)	Zirconium
Monel		

PLASTICS

Acetal Resin	Polyethylene	TFE (Teflon)
Kel-F	Polypropylene	Tygon
Nylon	Polyvinyl Chloride	

CHARACTERISTICS OF THE MOST WIDELY USED TUBING MATERIALS

Aluminum Tubing: Drawn seamless aluminum tubing is recommended for use with SWAGELOK Tube Fittings. An extruded seamless tube may also be used at some sacrifice of dimensional tolerances. Avoid using welded aluminum tube whenever possible. Alloy 5052-0 or alloy 6061-0 have superior corrosion resistance and tensile strength and are suitable for most applications. These alloys should always be used in the soft or annealed condition. Avoid tempers such as H14 — H16 — H18 — T6 and T4. In some instances 1100 or 3003 alloy tubing is used for purposes of economy. Buyers should carefully specify their requirements when purchasing 1100 or 3003 alloy since commodity products such as furniture tube not suitable for fluid applications, are often fabricated from these alloys. (See pressure rating tables in Appendix Section II of this manual.)

Characteristics to consider in the selection of aluminum tubing are its light weight, ease of bending and cutting, excellent corrosion resistance, and finishing properties. (See pressure rating tables in Appendix Section II of this manual.)

Copper Tubing: Copper tubing is seamless. It can be obtained fully annealed in coils or in straight lengths. Fully annealed tubing is recommended for use with brass SWAGELOK Tube Fittings. (See pressure rating tables in Appendex Section II of this manual.)

Carbon Steel Tubing: Carbon steel tubing is available as seamless or welded. Annealed, seamless hydraulic steel tubing should be used for fluid systems in conjunction with steel SWAGELOK Tube Fittings. Examples of such tubing are SAE or JIC hydraulic tubing, AMS-5050, or ASTM A179 steel tubing. JIC recommends a maximum hardness of Rockwell B65 and ASTM A179 allows a maximum hardness of Rockwell B72. Tubing harder than these Rockwell values should not be used. Harder tubing will not furnish sufficient ductility to bend properly or permit the most efficient connections. USE STEEL TUBING WITH MAXIMUM HARDNESS ROCKWELL B72. (See pressure rating tables in Appendix Section II of this manual.)

Monel Tubing: Monel tubing is available in three grades, as follows:

1. *Standard Monel* — The standard grade of Monel tubing is used as an all purpose material with good resistance to erosion and corrosives. Primary use is for chemical processing equipment, condensers and heat exchangers, ship machinery, etc. This is available in both seamless and welded form.

2. *Type 403 Monel* — This type is non-magnetic either at or above room temperature and is well suited for pickling equipment, handling sulfuric acid solutions and vacuum tube structures. This alloy is available in the seamless form only.

3. *Type "K" Monel* — This type has a high corrosion resistance with high strength and hardness. It is used primarily for Bourdon Tube applications. This alloy is available in the seamless form only.

Fully annealed tubing with a maximum hardness of Rockwell B75 max. should be used with SWAGELOK Tube Fittings made of Monel.

Stainless Steel Tubing: Stainless steel tubing is available as seamless or welded and drawn. Annealed stainless steel tubing suitable for bending should be used with SWAGELOK 316 stainless steel fittings. ASTM A269 stainless steel tubing of high quality with preferably a hardness of Rockwell B75 and a maximum hardness of Rockwell B80 will provide reliable stainless steel tubing installations. USE STAINLESS STEEL TUBING WITH MAXIMUM HARDNESS ROCKWELL B80. When higher temperatures are involved consult tables on Allowable Working Pressures in this manual. (see Appendix Section II).

Corrosion: The corrosion resistance required is determined by the fluid to be contained, other materials in the system, temperatures, and sometimes, external conditions such as atmospheric contaminants. Corrosion resistance is the most complex of the material properties to consider in selecting a material. In selecting a material for corrosive application, it is necessary to have considerable understanding of the theories and variables important to corrosion problems. These include chemical attack, galvanic action, dezincification, oxygen cell corrosion, stress corrosion and other forms of intergranular attack. Copper tubing with brass fittings and steel tubing with steel fittings are generally limited to inert fluids such as oil, water, air and non-corrosive gases. 316 stainless steel can be used for more corrosive and dangerous acids, or radioactive water.

A table of corrosion resistance is given in Section III of the Appendix for general guidance.

Temperature: Temperature restricts the use of metals because of loss of strength at higher temperatures, due to metallurgical changes that may take place, and increased corrosion rates at the higher temperatures. Generally, copper with brass should be limited to about 400°F. Steel can be used to 950°F, but metallurgical problems can occur if operation above 750°F occurs over a long period of time. 316 stainless steel can be used to about 1600°F to 1800°F, but system conditions and corrosion at these high temperatures must be considered for such applications. 304 stainless steel can be used up to about 1400°F to 1500°F with extreme care, and only after an extensive engineering investigation has been made.

The following graph shows the strength reduction in Monel, stainless steel, steel, copper and aluminum as temperature increases.

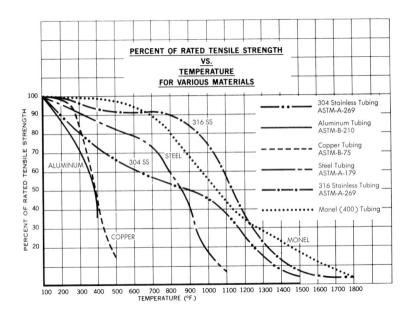

Fig. 33
Strength reduction versus temperature for
various tubing materials.

NOTE: For more detailed information on pressure ratings refer to the Appendix, Section II of this manual.

Based upon strength reduction, the approximate limiting temperatures for tubing materials are given below:

Material	Approx. Limiting Temperature
Stainless Steel 304	1200°F
Stainless Steel 316	1400°F
Monel	1100°F
Carbon Steel	950°F
Copper and Brass	400°F
Aluminum	400°F
TFE	450°F
Nylon	180°F
Polyvinyl Chloride (PVC) (Tygon)	165°F
Polyethylene	150°F

Stress: Generally, in tubing applications, the major stress is the result of internal pressure. The strength of the tubing determines the amount of stress that can be withstood. Copper has lower tensile strength than steel, and steel has lower tensile strength than stainless steel. As system pressure increases, it is necessary to use heavier wall tubing or stronger material. Unreasonable tube wall thickness determines the pressures at which steel should be substituted for copper and brass, or stainless steel substituted for steel.

The strength of a material is expressed by tensile or ultimate strength and by yield strength. The yield strength of a material is important because, if a material is subjected to stress beyond yield, a permanent set is taken by the material. In general, systems are designed never to reach yield conditions.

If stress equal to tensile strength is reached, failure of the tubing material occurs. Approximate tensile and yield strengths at room temperature are shown on page 32.

Tubing Material	Ultimate or Tensile Strength Lbs. per sq. in.	Yield strength Lbs. per sq. in.
Stainless Steel 316 & 304 (Annealed)	75,000 to 80,000	30,000 to 40,000
Monel (Annealed)	70,000 to 85,000	25,000 to 40,000
Carbon Steel (Annealed)	47,000	22,500
Copper (Annealed)	32,000	10,000
Aluminum (5052-0)	25,000	10,000
Nylon	11,000	not available
Polyvinyl Chloride	6,000 to 8,000	not available
Polyethylene	2,500	not available
TFE	2,000	not available

SWAGELOK Tube Fitting Materials: SWAGELOK Tube Fittings are available in any machineable metal or plastic.

Listed below are a few of the metals and plastics from which SWAGELOK Fittings have been manufactured.

MATERIALS — (Metal)

A286 Alloy Steel
Aluminum Alloys
Brass
CMF22 Chrome Moly Steel
Gold/24 Carat
Hastelloy/Alloy B
Hastelloy/Alloy C-276
Hastelloy/Alloy X
Haynes #25
Inconel 600
Inconel X
Lead
Magnesium Alloys
Molybdenum
Monel
Nickel
Carpenter 20 Cb3 Stainless Steel
Carpenter 455 Stainless Steel

17-4PH Stainless Steel
302   Stainless Steel
303   Stainless Steel
304   Stainless Steel
304L Stainless Steel
310   Stainless Steel
316   Stainless Steel
316L Stainless Steel
321   Stainless Steel
347   Stainless Steel
416   Stainless Steel
22-13-5 Stainless Steel
Steel (Carbon)
Tantalum
Titanium
Zirconium
Zirconium Alloys

MATERIALS — (Plastic)

Acetal
Nylon
PCTFE Fluorocarbon (Kel-F)
Polyethylene

Polypropylene
Polyvinyl Chloride
TFE Fluorocarbon

In the common applications of brass fittings with copper tubing, carbon steel fittings with carbon steel tubing and stainless steel fittings with stainless steel tubing, the fitting design takes strength and size into account and the required swaging action is obtained when used with proper tubing.

The availability of plastic fittings and ferrules allows more variety of applications such as connection to glass. A variety of combinations of tubing and fitting materials is given below to aid in proper ferrule selection to obtain the best results and corrosion compatability.

Tubing Material	Body	Front Ferrule	Back Ferrule
GLASS	TFE*	TFE	Nylon if temp. below 180°F 316 SS if above 180°F
	Polyethylene*	Polyethylene	Nylon
	Nylon	TFE	Nylon
	Metal	TFE	Nylon or Metal (see above)
	CAJON Ultra-Torr (See Vacuum Section)		
TFE	TFE*	TFE	316 SS
POLYETHYLENE	Nylon	Nylon	Nylon
	Polyethylene*	Polyethylene	Nylon
	Metal	Metal	Metal
NYLON	Nylon	Metal or Nylon	Metal
	Metal	Metal	Metal
PLASTICIZED PVC or TYGON**	Nylon	Nylon	Nylon
	Polyethylene*	Polyethylene	Polyethylene
	Metal	Metal	Metal
	CAJON Hose Connectors (See Pipe Fitting Section)		

*For more permanent type connections than usual laboratory work, it is found that a tighter grip on tubing can be obtained by using a metal nut on TFE and polyethylene fittings.
**Brass, 316 SS or Nylon inserts should be used with these very soft types of tubing.

TUBE SIZING

Inside Diameter (I. D.): The I. D. of tubing is set by flow requirements, permissible pressure drop and velocity. Charts for selecting I.D. knowing the flow, pressure drop and velocity requirements are given in Section I of the appendix.

Outside Diameter (O. D.): The O.D. of tubing is set by determining the I. D., then determining the wall thickness required for system operating pressure. Tables for selecting tubing for various working pressures are given in Section II of the appendix.

Manufacturing Tolerances of tubing: It is generally accepted that tolerances for tubing manufacture can vary in ASTM specifications for the various ferrous, non-ferrous and corrosion resistant alloy tubing. The following commercial tolerances for outside diameter and nominal wall thickness should not be exceeded for metal tubing.

Good quality polyethylene tubing, TFE and nylon can be used with SWAGELOK Tube Fittings.

MANUFACTURING TOLERANCES OF TUBING

Outside Diameter Range	Tolerance on Outside Diameter	Tolerance on Nominal Wall
Up to but not including $\frac{3}{32}''$ O. D.	+ 0.002″ − 0.000	± 10%
$\frac{3}{32}''$ to, but not including $\frac{3}{16}''$ O. D.	+ 0.003″ − 0.000	± 10%
$\frac{3}{16}''$ to, but not including $\frac{1}{2}''$ O. D.	+ 0.004″ − 0.000	± 10%
$\frac{1}{2}''$ to, but not including $1\frac{1}{2}''$ O. D.	+ 0.005″ − 0.000	± 10%
$1\frac{1}{2}''$ to, but not including $3\frac{1}{2}''$ O. D.	+ 0.010″ − 0.000	± 10%

PRECAUTIONS WITH TUBING

1. Handle tubing with care at all times.
2. Purchase tubing with capped or crimped ends to insure internal cleanliness.
3. Be sure tubing is annealed (soft) tubing. (Hardened types are not recommended for hydraulic or pressure applications.)
4. Do not drag straight lengths of tubing from storage racks in such a manner as to produce deep scratches along the length of the tubing. Such scratches could cause leaks when connected.
5. Do not uncoil more tubing than is needed. Uncoiling and recoiling will work harden tubing.
6. Remember that the tubing you use has been manufactured to close tolerances. Do not let rough handling destroy the quality that has been purchased.

TUBE PREPARATION

Prior to attaching fittings to tubing, it is necessary to take certain preparatory steps with the tubing.

Preparatory Steps
1. Uncoil tubing.
2. Cut tubing.
3. Deburr tubing.
4. Bend tubing.

HOW TO UNCOIL TUBING

Fig. 34

Take the end of the tubing and, with the right hand hold it down on a flat surface such as a table top, wooden plank, floor or sidewalk. If flat surface is rough, put padding down to protect end of tubing from scratches.

Fig. 35

Commence rolling the coil away from the end of the tubing with the left hand.

Fig. 36

Slide the right hand along the tubing, following the coil in such a manner that the tubing lies flat on the flat surface. Do not pull to straighten, since the O.D. can be reduced and may cause problems.

Do not uncoil more tubing than is necessary, since repeated uncoiling and recoiling will distort, harden and stiffen tubing.

HOW TO CUT TUBING

When available, use a tube cutter to cut the tubing. When cutting off a long piece of tubing, rock the tube cutter with your hand first going above the tubing (Fig. 37) then back around so that your hand goes below the tubing (Fig. 38) which will allow you to cut the tubing without taking your hand off the tube cutter. The cutter handwheel can be adjusted as the rocking proceeds to maintain even tension on the cutting wheel. When cutting a short piece of tubing, the cutter may be continually rotated around the end of the tubing. The handwheel can be gradually rotated to maintain even tension on the cutting wheel.

It is important that the cutting wheel be in top condition and it is recommended that a spare, sharp cutting wheel be kept available at all times.

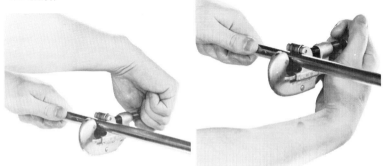

Fig. 37   Fig. 38
Proper use of tube cutter.

If a tube cutter of the proper size is not available, a hacksaw can be used (see Fig. 39). Tubing should always be cut to length with a square cut. When using a hacksaw to cut tubing, guide-blocks are desirable to insure a square cut and to keep the tubing from flattening out.

Do not use undue pressure when cutting soft tubing such as aluminum or copper with a hacksaw. Unless care is taken, the tube will flatten.

Fig. 39
Hacksaw and guideblocks used to cut tubing.

The cutters throw a burr into the I. D. of the tubing (see Fig. 40) and a hacksaw will burr both the I. D. and O. D. of the tube (see Fig. 41). These burrs should be removed after cutting the tube. Make sure that chips of metal are cleaned from the end of the tubing as metal chips can cause a fitting to leak or cause damage to components in the system.

Fig. 40   Fig. 41
Tube cutter burrs — I.D.   Hacksaw burrs — I.D. and O.D.

HOW TO DEBURR TUBING

Scrapers or half-round files will clear the I. D. of tubing of objectionable burrs without causing damage to the tubing (see Fig. 42).

Fig. 42
Removal of I.D. burrs with file.

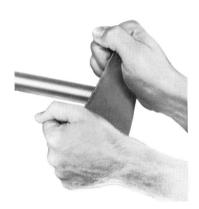

Fig. 43

The flat side of a file or emery cloth can be used to dress up O. D. burrs (see Fig. 43). Dress the burr by keeping the file or emery cloth at about a 45° angle with the tube. Do not scratch the tube surface.

If a rough cut has been made, it is sometimes necessary to dress and square the tube end.

BENDING TUBING

One of the greatest advantages of tubing is that it can be bent. Though bending to a radius of 2 or 3 times the tube diameter is possible, proper procedures must be used or difficulties such as flattening, kinking or wrinkling will occur. (see Fig. 44).

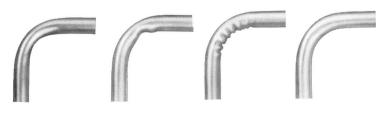

| Flattened Bend | Kinked Bend | Wrinkled Bend | Good 90° Bend |

Fig. 44

When such difficulties are encountered, they are usually caused by bending too short a radius, not using or improperly using a mandrel on thin wall tubing, or slippage in the tube bender. Bending of tubing may be accomplished by hand, by hand benders, or by production benders.

HAND BENDING

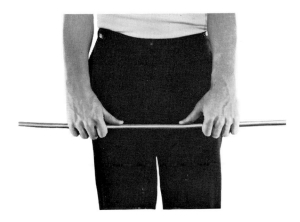

Fig. 45

Hand bending is accomplished by placing the thumbs towards each other, but far enough apart to allow length for making the bend.

Fig. 46

Bend the tubing slightly.

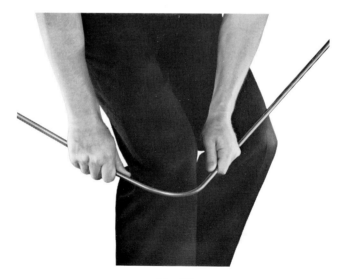

Fig. 47

Use your knee as a bending form (see Fig. 47) and bend tubing in small increments by shifting knee to various points on the inside of the bend. Coiled springs inside or outside such a bend help prevent deforming the tube. Hand bending to a small radius is very difficult as flattening usually results.

HAND BENDERS AND PRODUCTION BENDERS

Hand benders and production benders are either the compression or the draw type.

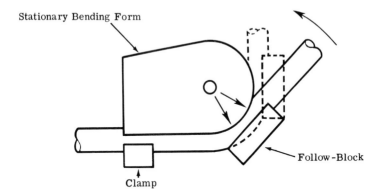

Fig. 48
Compression Type Tube Bender

In the compression type tube bender, the form is stationary and the follow-block rotates around to bend the tube. The portion of tubing to the left remains stationary.

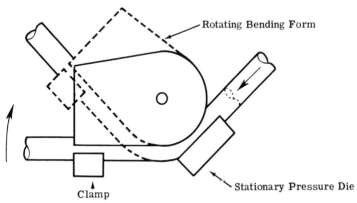

Fig. 49
Draw Type Tube Bender

In the draw type tube bender, the form moves and the end of the tubing to the left moves with the form. The tubing to the right is drawn past the stationary pressure die.

HAND BENDERS

The steps in making a bend with a hand bender are shown in Figs. 50, 51, 52 and 53.

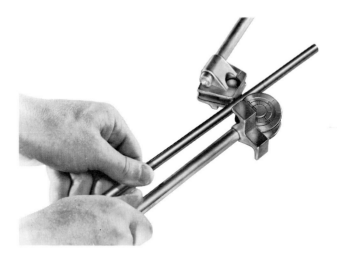

Fig. 50

The tubing is inserted in the bender.

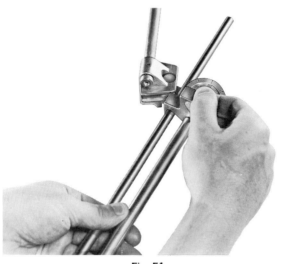

Fig. 51

The clamp is placed over the tube.

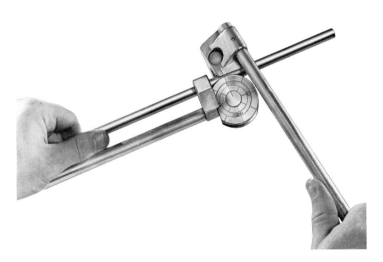

Fig. 52

The bending handle is moved into place.

Fig. 53

The handles are brought together to bend the tube and bending is stopped when the desired angle of bend is shown on bender indicator.

PRODUCTION BENDER

For production runs and intricate bends, a good quality production tube bender is recommended. Pictured below is an example of such a tool.

Fig. 54

Production Bender

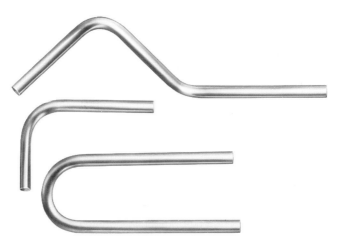

Fig. 55

Selection of different types of bends that can be made with
Production Bender.

MINIMUM RADIUS OF BEND

Radius of Bend is defined to be the radius to the center of the tube. (see Fig. 56).

The table below gives a radius that can be obtained if proper tubing and equipment are used. Column "A" gives the smallest bend that can be obtained utilizing the greatest care and best equipment on copper tubing. Column "B" gives radii that can usually be obtained without using a mandrel. The range of column "B" covers annealed steel and stainless steel tubing in addition to copper tubing.

Tube O.D. Diameter (inches)	A Minimum Tube Bend Radius Optimum Conditions (inches)	B Minimum Tube Bend Radius Without Mandrel (inches)
⅛ "	.250"	.500"
¼ "	.500"	1.000"
⅜ "	.750"	1.500" to 2.000"
½ "	1.000"	1.500" to 2.000"
⅝ "	1.250"	1.500" to 2.000"
¾ "	1.500"	3.000"
⅞ "	1.750"	3.500"
1 "	2.000"	4.000"
1¼ "	2.500"	2.500"
1½ "	3.000"	3.000"
2"	4.000"	4.000"

Material, tube wall thickness and equipment used will influence the smallest bend possible. The above table is only an indication of bends that can be expected. Follow the recommendations of the manufacturers of the tube bender and tubing when attempting to obtain minimum radius bends.

BENDS NEAR TUBE FITTINGS

Tube bending should be performed before connecting fittings. If bending is necessary after connecting to a fitting, care should be taken that the fitting is not used as an anchor or holding device to perform the bending operation.

Improper tube bending close to a fitting installation may be a source of leaks and care must be used on such installations. Several precautions should be taken:

BENDS NEAR TUBE FITTINGS (Continued)

1. Leave a length of straight tube so that the deformed section at a bend does not enter the fitting. (See recommended length of straight tube in Fig. 56).

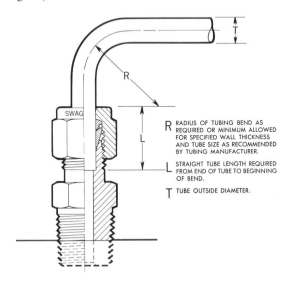

R RADIUS OF TUBING BEND AS REQUIRED OR MINIMUM ALLOWED FOR SPECIFIED WALL THICKNESS AND TUBE SIZE AS RECOMMENDED BY TUBING MANUFACTURER.

L STRAIGHT TUBE LENGTH REQUIRED FROM END OF TUBE TO BEGINNING OF BEND.

T TUBE OUTSIDE DIAMETER.

Fig. 56

T Tube O.D.		$\frac{1}{16}$	$\frac{1}{8}$	$\frac{3}{16}$	$\frac{1}{4}$	$\frac{5}{16}$	$\frac{3}{8}$	$\frac{1}{2}$	$\frac{5}{8}$	$\frac{3}{4}$	$\frac{7}{8}$	1 in.	$1\frac{1}{4}$	$1\frac{1}{2}$	2
L Length of Straight Tube	A*	$\frac{1}{2}$	$\frac{23}{32}$	$\frac{3}{4}$	$\frac{13}{16}$	$\frac{7}{8}$	$\frac{15}{16}$	$1\frac{3}{16}$	$1\frac{1}{4}$	$1\frac{1}{4}$	$1\frac{5}{16}$	$1\frac{1}{2}$	2	$2\frac{13}{32}$	$3\frac{1}{4}$
	B*	$\frac{13}{32}$	$\frac{19}{32}$	$\frac{5}{8}$	$\frac{11}{16}$	$\frac{23}{32}$	$\frac{3}{4}$	$\frac{31}{32}$	$1\frac{1}{32}$	$1\frac{1}{32}$	$1\frac{3}{32}$	$1\frac{9}{32}$	$1\frac{13}{16}$	$2\frac{7}{32}$	$3\frac{1}{32}$
R		Radius of tube bend as recommended by tubing manufacturer.													

*NOTE: Dimensions in Row A represent recommended straight tube length. Dimensions in Row B to be used when an absolute minimum straight tube length is necessary.

2. Inspect, for proper roundness, the length of tube that will be inserted into a fitting. Out-of-round tubing could scratch when entering fitting, resulting in leaks.

3. Long runs of tubing should be supported as should all other components.

4. When a section of bent tubing is being connected, be certain that the tube is in proper alignment with the fitting before doing any tightening. Springing the tube into position with the fitting can result in excessive stress on the tubing and the connection.

5. Make proper bends in the tubing and proper alignment will insure a good, trouble-free connection.

STRENGTH OF TUBING BEND:

No allowance should be made for the thinning of the tube wall at a bend. A bend in a section of tubing actually has greater strength than the straight run portion due to a work hardening of the material.

Fig. 57 shows what happens when a bend is subjected to a hydraulic pressure test. Note that the unbent tubing has been burst in one straight section and yielded to almost the bursting point in the other straight section while the bend is still in its original form.

Fig. 57

Tubing fails on straight portion showing increase of tensile strength of material at the outside of the bend.

CHAPTER III

TUBING INSTALLATION

When installing a system, the first step is to draw a layout of the system to determine the number of tube fittings and the length of tubing required. Care in determining the tube run will save time and possible re-running at a later date. Points to be remembered are enumerated below.

1. Tubing should be run clear of access doors, bolts and equipment that must have access for maintenance (see Fig. 58 & 59).

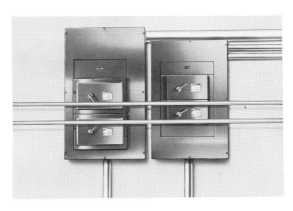

Fig. 58

Wrong. Fuse panel blocked.

Fig. 59

Right. Fuse panel clear.

2. When tubing is attached to an item that must occasionally be removed for repair or maintenance, the method of connecting and
running the tubing should permit easy removal (see Fig. 60-61).

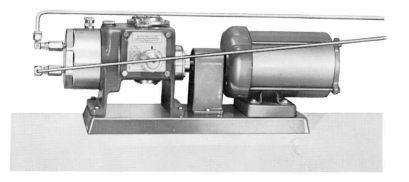

Fig. 60

Wrong. Neither pump nor motor is accessible for maintenance.

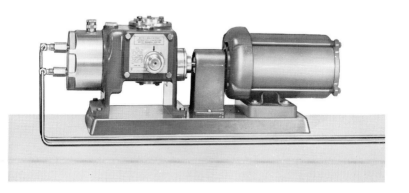

Fig. 61

Right. Pump unit connected properly to permit access.

3. Tubing should be kept clear of controls and not impede the operator's access to controls (see Fig. 62).

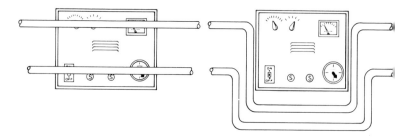

Fig. 62
Wrong. Operating panel blocked.   Right. Operating panel clear.

4. Mechanical damage can often be avoided if one remembers that there is a temptation to use a low run as a bar rail for resting feet (see Fig. 63). A potential danger also exists in high runs. A high run at 6 or 7 feet can be used like a bus rail (see Fig. 64).

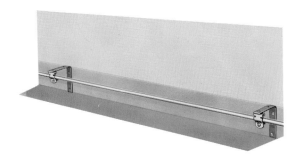

Fig. 63
Bar Rail

Fig. 64
Bus Rail

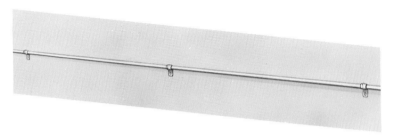

Fig. 65
Correct mounting

5. Tubing should be supported in long runs to prevent sagging. Fluid density and tube size determine the frequency of supports. Generally, such supports should allow free axial movement of the tubing and only support the weight of the tubing (see Fig. 66). All components should be mounted. The tubing should not support the weight of valves, filters, regulators, etc., (see Fig. 67). ¼″ through ½″ tubing should be supported every 3 feet, ⅝″ through ⅞″ tubing about every 5 feet and 1″ and larger about every 7 feet.

Fig. 66
Tubing supported in
long run

Fig. 67
Lubricator with angle
bracket support

6. Valves or other devices that require torque to be exerted in their operation should be mounted so that a twisting movement is not applied to the tubing. (see Fig. 68-69).

Fig. 68

Wrong. Strain is placed on tubing because valve is not restrained.

Fig. 69

Right. When valve is mounted to prevent rotation of the valve body, no strain is placed on the tubing.

7. Tubing should be ganged vertically rather than horizontally to avoid collection of dirt and corrosive conditions (see Fig. 70-71).

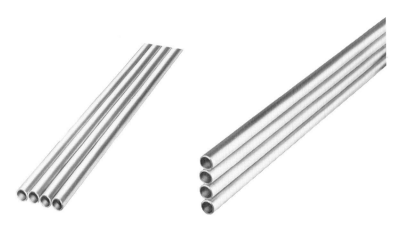

Fig. 70
Avoid this

Fig. 71
Correct method

If it is necessary to gang horizontally, the tubing should be covered.

8. Fittings should be staggered and offset when making multiple runs to provide easier installation and conserve space (see Fig. 72-73).

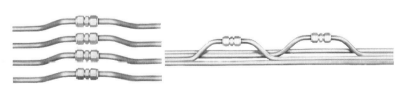

Fig. 72
Wrong. Space wasted

Fig. 73
Right. Installation is neater and space is conserved

9. Expansion loops should be installed to prevent tension stresses and allow for temperature expansion (see Fig. 74-75).

WRONG   WRONG

Fig. 74

Wrong. Installations made like this will eventually leak because of movement of the tubing from temperature changes.

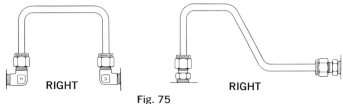

RIGHT   RIGHT

Fig. 75

Right. Installations of this type allow for expansion from day to day temperature changes and allow easy disassembly.

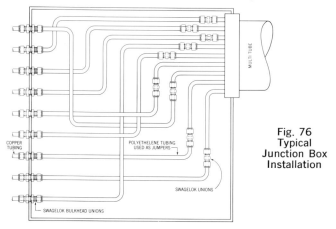

Fig. 76
Typical
Junction Box
Installation

Taking into account the above points, the next step is to measure the run. First, determine the type of terminal connections to be used and, from the dimensions given in the SWAGELOK Tube Fitting catalog, determine the end point of the tubing (see Fig. 77).

Fig. 77
End point of tubing

Then make a layout sketch at the tube run by measuring distances with a flexible steel rule. This can be done by measuring all bends as square as shown in Fig. 78. Measure all dimensions to tubing centerlines. For clearances, it is necessary to allow for one-half the tubing diameter to clear obstructions. In the following example, assume that ½″ O.D. tubing is to be used (see Fig. 78).

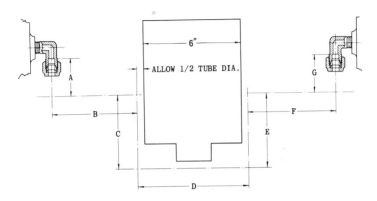

Fig. 78

The length of the tubing required is roughly the sum of dimensions A, B, C, D, E, F, and G. For example, using numbers;
A(3″) + B(8″) + C(6″) + D(7″) + E(6″) + F(10″) + G (3″), the total length would be 43″.

A more accurate tube length can be obtained by actually figuring the lengths with bends. To do this, the diameter of the bends would be determined depending upon the tubing to be used and the type bending equipment to be employed. Assuming a bend radius of 1″, the layout then becomes:

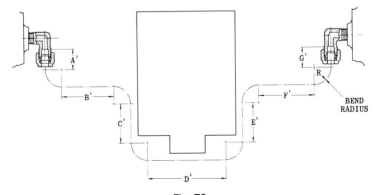

Fig. 79

Where:
$$A' = A - 1 = 3 - 1 = 2''$$ $$D' = D - 2 = 7 - 2 = 5''$$
$$B' = B - 2 = 8 - 2 = 6''$$ $$E' = E - 2 = 6 - 2 = 4''$$
$$C' = C - 2 = 6 - 2 = 4''$$ $$F' = F - 2 = 10 - 2 = 8''$$
$$G' = G - 1 = 3 - 1 = 2''$$

The total straight length would be 31".

To this length must be added the length of the tubing required for (6) 90°bends. The length of tubing in a 90° bend is equal to 1.57 times the radius of the bend, or:

Length of tubing in 90° bend = 1.57 × bend radius
For a bend radius of 1", which we assumed above.

Length of tubing in 90° bend = 1.57×1" or 1.57 inches
For six (6) 90° bends, six times this length is needed, that is:
6 × 1.57" = 9.42 inches.

BEND RADIUS

ANGLE	FACTOR	(x) BEND RADIUS (VARIABLE)	
30°	0.52	''	LENGTH OF TUBING IN A BEND
45°	0.78	''	
60°	1.04	''	
90°	1.57	''	
180°	3.14	''	

The total length of tubing needed is the sum of the bend length and straight length measured above, or:

Total length = straight length + bend lengths or
31" + 9.42" = 40.42 inches.

As can be seen from this example, runs can be roughly sized by measuring straight lengths, assuming square corners and the excess tubing trimmed off after bending.

Having cut the piece of tubing to a length of 43", it is now necessary to bend the tubing to make the installation.

Step 1. Measure from the end of the tubing the length A (3") and mark the tubing (see Fig. 80).

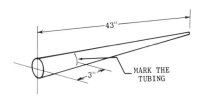

Fig. 80

Step 2. Align the scribe mark tangent to the 90° mark on the bender (see Fig. 81).

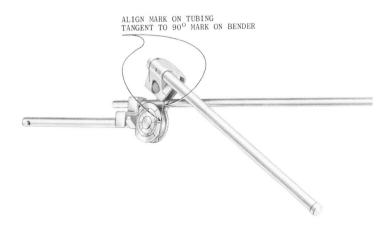

ALIGN MARK ON TUBING
TANGENT TO 90° MARK ON BENDER

Fig. 81

Step 3. Then bend the tubing until the bender indicates a 90° bend (see Fig. 82).

Fig. 82

The centerline dimension from the end of the tubing to the center-line of the bent tubing is 3″, since the bender holds ½ the diameter of the tubing in the bending die (see Fig. 83).

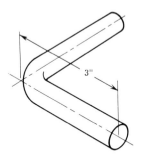

Fig. 83

Step 4.   Then measure length B, (8″ from the tube centerline) and again mark the tubing (see Fig. 84).

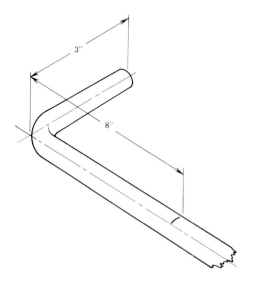

Fig. 84

Step 5.   As in steps 2 and 3, align the bender and make the second bend (see Fig. 85).

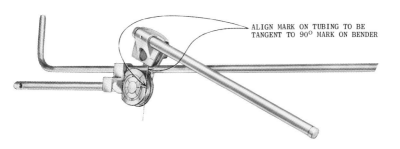

ALIGN MARK ON TUBING TO BE
TANGENT TO 90° MARK ON BENDER

Fig. 85

Repeat this procedure by measuring from centerline, C, D, E, F, and G, (see page 55) turning the tubing over as necessary to position the tube bender.

When the tubing has reached its final shape, length G will be a little long since we started with a 43″ tube length.

Check the tubing in the proposed installation by placing it alongside the two terminal connections. Scribe the tubing for the amount to trim off, trim tubing with a tube cutter, ream I.D., and then install into the tube fittings (see Fig. 86).

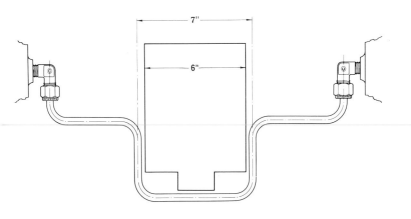

Fig. 86

Tighten the SWAGELOK Tube Fitting as previously instructed, and the installation is complete. Notice the need for allowing one-half the tubing diameter for clearance when length **D** was determined. However, your own personal preference will determine the clearance desired.

USE OF *SWAGELOK* ADAPTERS

Anyone who has installed pipe elbows, tees or valves with pipe connections at a terminal point of a system or on a component is acquainted with the difficulty of aligning the fitting with the desired tubing run or of properly locating the valve handle. When the pipe thread is tight, the fitting is often pointing in the opposite direction intended for the tubing run or the valve handle is located in a poor position. Loosening the pipe connection means leakage at the pipe thread which is an unsatisfactory solution. Tightening can result in stripped threads, leaks, and banged-up knuckles.

The SWAGELOK Adapters were specifically designed with this problem in mind. By using an adapter and then a union elbow the above difficulty is avoided, frustration eliminated and money saved.

(Applications of this type are shown in Fig. 87 through 92).

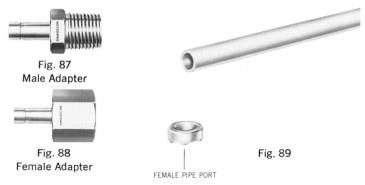

Fig. 87
Male Adapter

Fig. 88
Female Adapter

FEMALE PIPE PORT

Fig. 89

Required installation is to connect tubing in direction shown, to a female port.

MALE ELBOW

Fig. 90

With pipe connection tight, the male elbow is pointing in the wrong direction for desired tubing run.

USE OF *SWAGELOK* ADAPTER

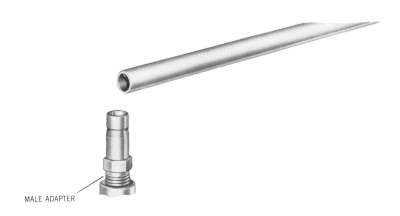

Fig. 91

To correct this situation, merely tighten pipe thread of male adapter into female port.

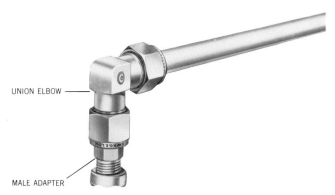

Fig. 92

Connect union elbow to adapter by tightening SWAGELOK connection with wrench while holding elbow pointing in desired direction. Then insert tubing into the other end of the SWAGELOK Union Elbow and connect tubing.

Another application of SWAGELOK Adapters would be to use adapters to properly align the elbows in the example we used to lay out a tubing run. (Use shorter "B" and "F" dimensions as necessary, see Fig. 78).

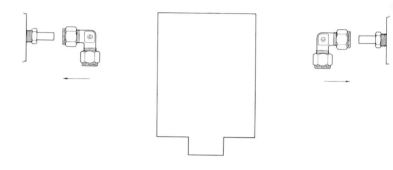

Fig. 93

Align elbows and tighten SWAGELOK nut according to installation instructions.

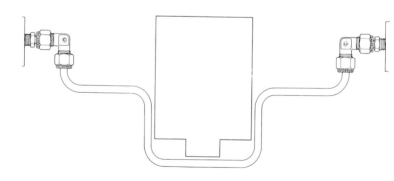

Fig. 94

Install the tubing run to the elbows thus completing the installation.

The SWAGELOK Adapter fitting is found particularly advantageous for ease of alignment when connecting tees or elbows behind a bulkhead. Examples of this type of application are shown in Fig. 95.

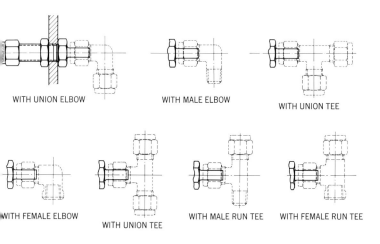

WITH UNION ELBOW   WITH MALE ELBOW   WITH UNION TEE

WITH FEMALE ELBOW   WITH UNION TEE   WITH MALE RUN TEE   WITH FEMALE RUN TEE

Fig. 95

Applications of Bulkhead Adapters with standard SWAGELOK Fittings.

USE OF *SWAGELOK* ADAPTERS FOR VALVE INSTALLATIONS

When installing a valve, there is usually a preferred location for the valve handle. For example, coming off a piece of equipment, it is often desired to have the valve handle located directly above the valve as shown in Fig. 96.

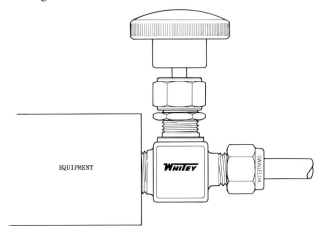

EQUIPMENT

Fig. 96

If the connection provided on the equipment is a male or female pipe thread, obtaining the preferred handle location with a pipe end valve is extremely difficult if not impossible. The result is usually something like Fig. 97.

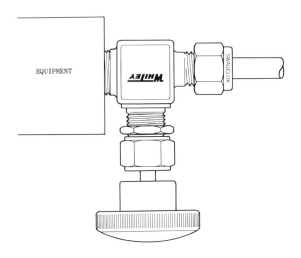

Fig. 97

To save time, stop leaks and prevent valve damage during installation, a male or female adapter should be used (see Figs. 98-99).

Fig. 98
Male Adapter

Fig. 99
Female Adapter

To orient your valve, screw the male adapter fitting into the equipment (see Fig. 100).

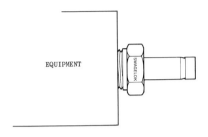

Fig. 100

Using a valve with **SWAGELOK** Tube Connections, slip the tubing stub from the adapter into one **SWAGELOK** connection, hold the valve vertical while pulling up the nut according to installation instructions and the valve is properly oriented (see Fig. 101).

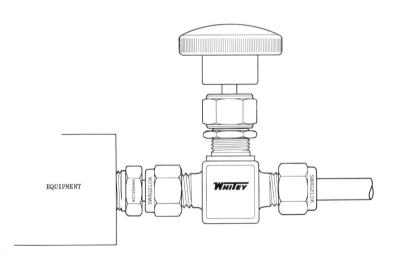

Fig. 101

If it is desired to shift the direction of the valve handle, all that is necessary is to loosen the nuts on the **SWAGELOK** connections, move and hold the valve at the desired handle location, and retighten the **SWAGELOK** nuts.

PORT CONNECTORS

Fig. 102
Port Connector

Fig. 103
Reducing Port Connector

INSTALLATION INSTRUCTIONS
1. Remove Nut and Ferrules from first of the two SWAGELOK Ports to be connected. 2. Slip Nut only (no Ferrules) on Port Connector over machined ferrule. 3. Insert Connector into first port and snug up Nut by hand. 4. Tighten with wrench $\frac{1}{4}$ turn only. Subsequent connections are made by tightening slightly with wrench after snugging the Nut by hand. 5. Insert second end of Port Connector into other port and tighten Nut $1\frac{1}{4}$ turns from finger-tight, using normal SWAGELOK Nut and Ferrules.

SWAGELOK Port Connectors are recommended for use where space is at a premium.

Features: Eliminates cutting short lengths of tubing • Allows close coupling with pre-determined lengths • No pipe threads in system • Effects a union at every joint to permit complete dis-assembly for removal from system • Machined from bar stock for rigidity and strength.

BULKHEAD CONNECTIONS

Only SWAGELOK has such a complete variety of Bulkhead Tube Fittings. Standard SWAGELOK Bulkhead Tube Fittings include: Bulkhead Unions • Bulkhead Adapters • Bulkhead Male Connectors • Bulkhead SWAGELOK to AN Unions • Bulkhead Female Connectors • Bulkhead Reducing Unions.

SWAGELOK Bulkhead Tube Fittings are available in sizes for $\frac{1}{16}''$ through 1″ O.D. tubing and can make leak-tight connections on a wide variety of tubing materials such as stainless steel, Monel, Nylon, TFE, aluminum, glass, copper, steel, etc.

SWAGELOK Bulkhead Tube Fittings, like all SWAGELOK Tube Fittings, are available in any machineable metal or plastic to meet your particular requirements.

BULKHEAD RETAINERS

Fig. 104
Bulkhead retainer

Bulkhead retainers are used to act as a backup wrench on the body hex of a bulkhead fitting, and are available in sizes from ⅛″ thru 1″.

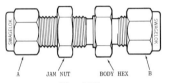

Fig. 105
Bulkhead fitting

To install a bulkhead fitting, it is usually necessary to have one man hold the body hex while another man tightens the jam nut (see Fig. 106).

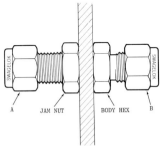

Fig. 106

Tubing can be connected to end B by one man holding the body hex and pulling up the fitting according to installation instructions. To pull up the fitting on end A, without a bulkhead retainer, it is necessary to put a man on side B to hold the body hex while a man on side A tightens the SWAGELOK Tube Fitting according to installation instructions.

By using the bulkhead retainer, one man can tighten the jam nut on side A for initial bulkhead installation. Tubing can now be connected to side A or B by one man with one wrench since the bulkhead retainer acts as a backup wrench (see Fig. 107).

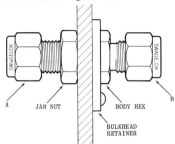

Fig. 107
Bulkhead installation utilizing bulkhead retainer.

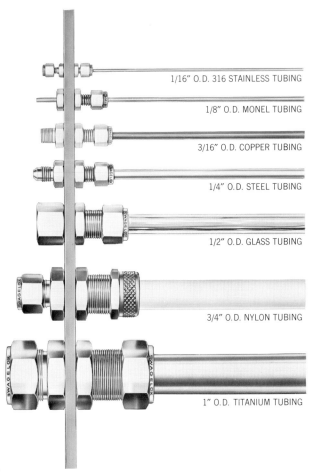

Fig. 108
Typical bulkhead material applications.

1/16" O.D. 316 STAINLESS TUBING

1/8" O.D. MONEL TUBING

3/16" O.D. COPPER TUBING

1/4" O.D. STEEL TUBING

1/2" O.D. GLASS TUBING

3/4" O.D. NYLON TUBING

1" O.D. TITANIUM TUBING

SWAGELOK O-SEAL FITTINGS

SWAGELOK O-Seal Fittings are manufactured within precise tolerances to control proper O-Ring squeeze, insuring helium leak-tightness
for vacuum applications. The fittings are designed so that when installed,
the O-Ring is completely retained by metal to prevent O-Ring extrusion.

Standard O-Ring is Buna compound. Other O-Ring materials are available on request.

Fig. 109
O-Seal Male Connector Pipe
Thread (Tapered)

Fig. 110
O-Seal Male Adapter Pipe
Thread (Tapered)

SWAGELOK O-Seal Connectors and Adapters with tapered pipe threads provide a vacuum-tight or high-pressure seal with existing pipe thread ports. O-Seal straight thread fittings are designed for use with straight thread ports to make similar leak-tight connections.

Other manufacturers produce a so-called "Dryseal" pipe thread. This thread uses substantial thread root and crest interference which theoretically perform a sealing function. In actual practice, it is almost always necessary to use a liquid or solid sealant for this purpose. (Refer to STRIP TEEZE Tape, Figs. 23-24).

Fig. 111
O-Seal Straight Thread Connector

Fig. 112
O-Seal Straight Thread Adapter

SWAGELOK O-Seal Straight Thread Fittings are designed for use with straight thread ports to make similar leak-tight connections.

INSTALLATION INSTRUCTIONS

In order to make a tight seal with SWAGELOK O-Seal Fittings, all that is necessary is to have a smooth flat surface for the O-Ring. It is very important that this surface be perpendicular to the axis of the threads.

When installing an O-Seal fitting, turn it until finger tight. (The squeeze on O-Ring can be felt during the last ¼ turn.) After finger tight installation, snug lightly with a wrench.

When connecting the tubing to the SWAGELOK connectors, always use a back-up wrench on the O-Seal fitting hex so that it does not turn while the nut is being tightened. Also use a back-up wrench when disconnecting a tubing connection.

For a raised surface, such as Figure A, it is recommended that the flat surface have a diameter at least as large as dimension "A" for the various size O-Seal fittings. This diameter is sufficient to allow metal to metal contact outside of the O-Ring sealing diameter, which will prevent O-Ring extrusion at high pressure.

Figure B is an O-Seal fitting used with a counterbored or recessed hole. In this case, the diameter "B" is sufficient to allow the round shoulder of the O-Seal to clear for proper installation. "D" gives the maximum depth that can be used with this diameter.

Figure C is a deeper counterbored or recessed hole and dimension "E" is the maximum depth that will allow a thin wrench (⅛") to hold the O-Seal fitting while the SWAGELOK connection is made to the tubing. The diameter "C" is sufficient to allow the hex of the fitting to turn in the recessed hole.

MOUNTING DIMENSIONS
FOR O-SEAL CONNECTORS AND ADAPTERS

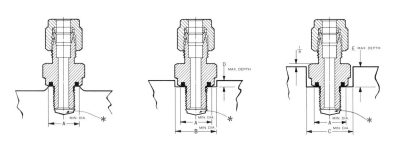

Fig. A   Fig. B   Fig. C
*ALLOW CLEARANCE FOR FULL THREAD

CATALOG NUMBER	Straight Thread	Pipe Thread	A Min. Dia. For Sealing	B Min. Dia.	D Max. Depth	C Min. Dia.	E Max. Depth
-100-1-OR	5/16-24		1/2	19/32	3/32	21/32	5/32
-100-1-1-OR		1/16 NPT	1/2	19/32	3/32	21/32	5/32
-200-1-OR	5/16-24		1/2	19/32	3/32	21/32	7/32
-200-1-2-OR		1/8 NPT	11/16	25/32	5/32	7/8	9/32
-300-1-OR	3/8-24		17/32	21/32	3/32	3/4	7/32
-400-1-OR	7/16-20		11/16	25/32	5/32	7/8	9/32
-400-1-4-OR		1/4 NPT	13/16	31/32	5/32	1 3/32	5/16
-500-1-OR	1/2-20		3/4	29/32	5/32	1 1/32	5/16
-600-1-OR	9/16-18		13/16	31/32	5/32	1 3/32	5/16
-600-1-6-OR		3/8 NPT	1	1 5/32	5/32	1 5/16	11/32
-810-1-OR	3/4-16		1	1 5/32	5/32	1 5/16	11/32
-810-1-8-OR		1/2 NPT	1 7/32	1 11/32	7/32	1 17/32	7/16
-1010-1-OR	7/8-14		1 7/32	1 11/32	7/32	1 17/32	7/16
-1210-1-OR	1 1/16-12		1 13/32	1 17/32	7/32	1 3/4	1/2
-1210-1-12-OR		3/4 NPT	1 13/32	1 17/32	7/32	1 3/4	1/2
-1410-1-OR	1 1/16-12		1 13/32	1 17/32	7/32	1 3/4	1/2
-1610-1-OR	1 5/16-12		1 11/16	1 25/32	7/32	2 1/32	9/16
-1610-1-16-OR		1" NPT	1 11/16	1 25/32	7/32	2 1/32	9/16

SPECIAL APPLICATION

SWAGELOK O-Seal Fittings are widely used to make connections to tapped holes on vessel walls or in sub-assemblies (see Figs. 113 & 114).

If vessel walls are too thin to permit tapping, a leak-tight seal can be obtained by using a jam nut with a SWAGELOK straight thread O-Seal Fitting (see Fig. 114).

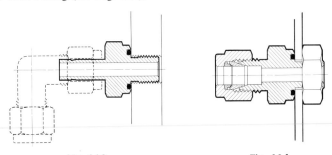

Fig. 113   Fig. 114

SWAGELOK TUBE FITTINGS FOR STRAIGHT THREAD BOSS

The hydraulic, automotive, marine and other allied industries require O-Seal type joints where the O-Ring is external to the body surface. In serving the ever growing needs of these industries SWAGELOK

Connectors and Adapters are designed for use with the following ports:

1. S.A.E.
2. J.I.C.
3. M.S. 33649 (Supersedes AND 10049 AND 10050)

Fig. 115

SWAGELOK Connector for Straight Thread Boss

CATALOG NUMBER	T TUBE O.D.	S THREAD SIZE	O-RING UNIFORM SIZE NUMBER
-200-1-2ST	⅛	⁵⁄₁₆-24	902
-300-1-3ST	³⁄₁₆	⅜-24	903
-400-1-4ST	¼	⁷⁄₁₆-20	904
-500-1-5ST	⁵⁄₁₆	½-20	905
-600-1-6ST	⅜	⁹⁄₁₆-18	906
-810-1-8ST	½	¾-16	908
-1010-1-10ST	⅝	⅞-17	910
-1210-1-12ST	¾	1¹⁄₁₆-12	912
-1410-1-14ST	⅞	1³⁄₁₆-12	914
-1610-1-16ST	1 in.	1⁵⁄₁₆-12	916
-2000-1-20ST	1¼	1⅝-12	920
-2400-1-24ST	1½	1⅞-12	924
-3200-1-32ST	2 in.	2½-12	932

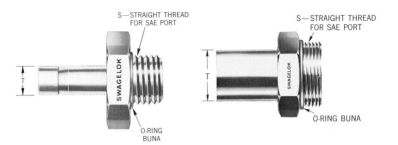

Fig. 116
1" and Under Adapter

Fig. 117
Over 1" Adapter

CATALOG NUMBER	T TUBE O.D.	S THREAD SIZE	O-RING UNIFORM SIZE NUMBER
-201-A-2ST	⅛	⁵⁄₁₆-24	902
-301-A-3ST	³⁄₁₆	⅜-24	903
-401-A-4ST	¼	⁷⁄₁₆-20	904
-501-A-5ST	⁵⁄₁₆	½-20	905
-601-A-6ST	⅜	⁹⁄₁₆-18	906
-811-A-8ST	½	¾-16	908
-1011-A-10ST	⅝	⅞-14	910
-1211-A-12ST	¾	1¹⁄₁₆-12	912
-1411-A-14ST	⅞	1³⁄₁₆-12	914
-1611-A-16ST	1 in.	1⁵⁄₁₆-12	916
-2001-A-20ST	1¼	1⅝-12	920
-2401-A-24ST	1½	1⅞-12	924
-3201-A-32ST	2 in.	2½-12	932

COMMERCIAL STRAIGHT THREAD TUBE FITTING BOSSES

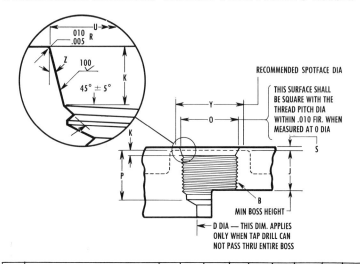

Nom Tube OD	Thread Size	B, Straight Thread				D Dia Min	J Full Thread Depth Min	K +0.015 -0.00 Min	O Dia Min	P □		S ●†	U* Dia +0.005 -0.000 Max	Yt Dia	Z ±1 Deg
		Pitch Dia		Minor Dia											
		Min	Max	Min	Max					Min	Max	Max			
$\frac{1}{8}$	$\frac{5}{16}$-24	0.2854	0.2902	0.267	0.277	0.062	0.390	0.074	0.438	0.468	0.062	0.358	0.672	12	
$\frac{3}{16}$	$\frac{3}{8}$-24	0.3479	0.3528	0.330	0.340	0.125	0.390	0.074	0.500	0.468	0.062	0.421	0.750	12	
$\frac{1}{4}$	$\frac{7}{16}$-20	0.4050	0.4104	0.383	0.395	0.172	0.454	0.093	0.563	0.547	0.062	0.487	0.828	12	
$\frac{5}{16}$	$\frac{1}{2}$-20	0.4675	0.4731	0.446	0.457	0.234	0.454	0.093	0.625	0.547	0.062	0.550	0.906	12	
$\frac{3}{8}$	$\frac{9}{16}$-18	0.5264	0.5323	0.502	0.515	0.297	0.500	0.097	0.688	0.609	0.062	0.616	0.969	12	
$\frac{1}{2}$	$\frac{3}{4}$-16	0.7094	0.7159	0.682	0.696	0.391	0.562	0.100	0.875	0.688	0.094	0.811	1.188	15	
$\frac{5}{8}$	$\frac{7}{8}$-14	0.8286	0.8356	0.798	0.814	0.484	0.656	0.100	1.000	0.781	0.094	0.942	1.344	15	
$\frac{3}{4}$	$1\frac{1}{16}$-12	1.0084	1.0158	0.972	0.900	0.609	0.750	0.130	1.250	0.906	0.094	1.148	1.625	15	
$\frac{7}{8}$	$1\frac{3}{16}$-12	1.1334	1.1409	1.097	1.115	0.719	0.750	0.130	1.375	0.906	0.094	1.273	1.765	15	
1	$1\frac{5}{16}$-12	1.2584	1.2659	1.222	1.240	0.844	0.750	0.130	1.500	0.906	0.125	1.398	1.910	15	
$1\frac{1}{4}$	$1\frac{5}{8}$-12	1.5709	1.5785	1.535	1.553	1.078	0.750	0.132	1.875	0.906	0.125	1.713	2.270	15	
$1\frac{1}{2}$	$1\frac{7}{8}$-12	1.8209	1.8287	1.785	1.803	1.312	0.750	0.132	2.125	0.906	0.125	1.962	2.560	15	
2	$2\frac{1}{2}$-12	2.4459	2.4540	2.410	2.428	1.781	0.750	0.132	2.750	0.906	0.125	2.587	3.480	15	

* Diameter U shall be concentric with thread pitch diameter within 0.005 full indicator reading (FIR), and shall be free from longitudinal and spiral tool marks. Annular tool marks up to 100 Mu in. max shall be permissable.

● Maximum recommended spotface depth to permit sufficient wrench grip for proper tightening of the fitting or locknut.

† If face of boss is on a machined surface, dimensions Y and S need not apply.

□ Tap drill depths given require use of bottoming taps to produce the specified full thread lengths. Where standard taps are used, the tap drill depths must be increased accordingly.

SWAGELOK INSPECTION GAUGE

The SWAGELOK Inspection Gauge is a device used to determine when most fittings have been properly tightened. It is designed to assist personnel in checking an installation. It is not a necessary part of the SWAGELOK installation. But more important, it is factual evidence of the close machining tolerances and high degree of quality control utilized in the manufacturing of SWAGELOK Tube Fittings.

Fig. 118
SWAGELOK Inspection Gauge.

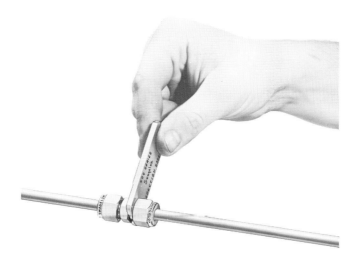

Fig. 119
Checking for high pressure service.

If the gauge fits between the SWAGELOK nut and the body hex of the fitting, it indicates that the fitting has not been sufficiently tightened.

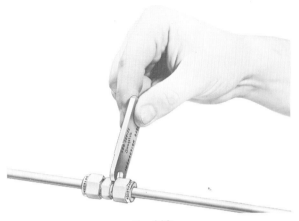

Fig. 120

If the gauge cannot be inserted between the SWAGELOK nut and the body hex, it indicates that the fitting has been sufficiently tightened. This inspection gauge can also be used on forgings that have a machined shoulder.

PLANNING AHEAD

Where extension of tubing runs or additional connections to air or hydraulic lines are probable, it is wise to use plugged tees, plugged unions or capped tubing so that the addition can be easily accommodated (see Fig. 120).

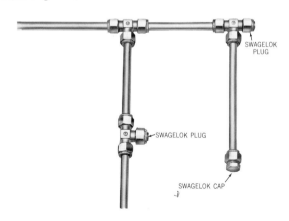

SWAGELOK
PLUG

SWAGELOK PLUG

SWAGELOK CAP

Fig. 121

USE OF ELBOWS FOR OFFSETS

Installation and maintenance time can be saved if union elbows are used for offsets rather than using a union.

Fig. 122
Standard method of offsetting

Fig. 123
Minimum bend method of offsetting using union elbow

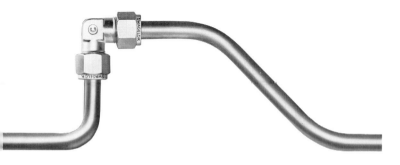

Fig. 124
Best method for ease of disconnecting an offset connection

CHAPTER IV

SPECIAL APPLICATIONS

1. STEAM TRACING

2. DOWTHERM "A" FLUID

3. DOWTHERM "E" FLUID

4. LIQUID SODIUM

5. VACUUM SYSTEMS

CHAPTER IV
SPECIAL APPLICATIONS

STEAM TRACING

Purpose: Steam tracing is a method of providing heat input to process lines and equipment to prevent freeze-up in cold weather. Tracing can also be applied to fluids that could become solid or extremely viscous, even in the summer months. This method is not covered in depth, since the amount of tracing required will vary with the application. An engineering analysis is recommended on viscous fluid tracing requirements. The severity of winters in a particular locale usually determines the need and methods of steam tracing. Of course, individual plant practices and preferences also influence requirements. The methods suggested in this manual are for guidance only.

Process lines and equipment can be protected from freezing by using tubing as the tracing lines. The most common steam tracing line sizes are ¼ " O.D. x .049 wall, ⅜ " O.D. x .049 wall, ½ " O.D. x .065 wall copper tubing.

On some installations, heavy wall tubing is preferred because the thicker wall gives improved performance during a cool-down period from full steam temperature and increases temperature cycling ability. It is during that time that thin wall tubing tries to shrink away from the fitting. Once this occurs any slight scratch becomes a potential leak path. The tubing should be a fully annealed quality.

TRACER INSTALLATION ON PROCESS LINES

Locating Horizontal Tracers: A variety of techniques has been developed for positioning the tracing lines in the best manner for suitable heat transfer. The tracing may be carried inside the pipe, or around it or beside it, depending on specific conditions. (see Fig. 125.) Always supply steam to tracers on the high end of a sloping process line to prevent back-up of condensate. As a general guide, small tracers should not exceed 60 feet in length and the limit for all other sizes should be about 150 feet.

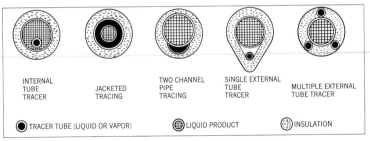

INTERNAL TUBE TRACER   JACKETED TRACING   TWO CHANNEL PIPE TRACING   SINGLE EXTERNAL TUBE TRACER   MULTIPLE EXTERNAL TUBE TRACER

TRACER TUBE (LIQUID OR VAPOR)   LIQUID PRODUCT   INSULATION

Fig. 125
Tracer location on horizontal or sloping lines.

The table below gives suggested information on the size and number of tracers for process lines of various sizes.

Process Pipe Size (in.)	Tracer Size**	No. of Tracers**	Max. Tracer Length	*Max. Tracer Length between Traps
1½″ and smaller	.049″ wall, ¼″ or ⅜″ O. D. Copper Tubing	1	60 ft.	60 ft.
2″ and 2½″	.065″ wall, ½″ O. D. Copper Tubing	1	150 ft.	150 ft.
3″ to 4″	″	2	″	″
6″ and 8″	″	3	″	″
10″ and 12″	″	4	″	″

*Use individual traps for each tracer line. Never manifold tracer lines to one trap.

**Or as required by individual needs.

Locating Vertical Tracers: A single tracer on a vertical or nearly vertical process line can be spiral wrapped. Multiple tracers on vertical lines should be equally spaced for the most efficient heat transfer. (see Fig. 126.)

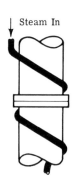
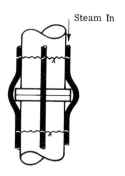

Single Tracer; Spiral Wrapped   Multiple Tracers; Equally spaced

Fig. 126
Tracer Installation on Vertical Lines

TRACER ATTACHMENT TO PROCESS LINES

Single Tracer: Use a soft galvanically compatible wire to attach tracer lines to process piping. Vertical lines with a spiral wrapped tracer do not require additional holding. Horizontal lines with ¼″ O. D. tracers should be tied every 1½ ft., while ½″ O.D. tracer lines should be tied every 2 ft. Tie wires should be equally spaced on each side of flanges. Always use a large radius bend *upward* when bringing the tracer line around a flange. (see Fig. 127.)

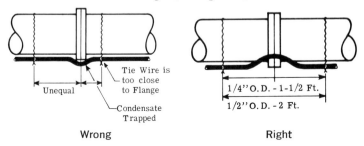

Wrong   Right

Fig. 127
Attachment of Tracer Line around flanges.

Multiple Tracers: When attaching multiple tracer lines to a process line, loop the tie wire around each tracer as shown in Fig. 128. This will prevent the tracer lines from sliding to the bottom of the process line.

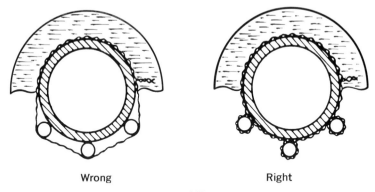

Wrong   Right

Fig. 128
Attachment of Multiple Tracers to a Process Line.

Expansion: Tracer tubing will expand as the temperature increases, as will the process piping when heat is transferred. The rates of expansion of the tracer tubing and the process line will usually be different. This is caused by the unlike coefficients of expansion of the two materials, and the temperature differential between the tracer and the process line. Sufficient slack in the tracer lines plus expansion bends are required to prevent the tracer tubing from stretching or kinking.

This can be done by providing expansion bends upward as shown in Fig. 127 and by applying the tracer as it comes from the tubing roll on straight portions of the process line. (See Fig. 129.) When tubing is uncoiled, small bends and irregularities exist which properly take up expansion or contraction of the tubing.

Fig. 129
View from bottom.
Tracer applied properly without straightening after uncoiling.

Tube Fittings: Brass SWAGELOK Tube Fittings are recommended for use on copper tracer lines (trace steam temperature up to 400° F), since they provide easy, reliable, leak-tight connections. Use carbon steel tubing and carbon steel SWAGELOK Tube Fittings for steam trace lines over 400° F. For maintenance ease, insulation should not be placed over the SWAGELOK Tube Fittings. Each SWAGELOK Tube Fitting is a union joint. Access to the fittings allows easy replacement of corroded or damaged tube sections. Wherever possible, locate the SWAGELOK Tube Fittings at the process pipe flanges or other uninsulated areas. When a SWAGELOK Tube Fitting must be used in an insulated area, provide a small window in the insulation for accessibility. (see Fig. 130.)

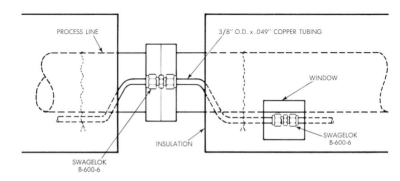

Fig. 130
Proper installation of SWAGELOK Tube Fittings on a Tracer Line.

TRACER INSTALLATION ON PROCESS EQUIPMENT

Two methods are available for installing tracers on irregularly shaped equipment such as valves, pumps and instruments. The two methods are Spiral Wrapped and Flat Grid.

Spiral Wrapping method: Approximately 6″ should be maintained between coils when the spiral wrapping method is used. Use SWAGELOK Unions to permit removal of the equipment without uncoiling the tracer line.

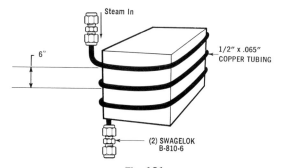

Fig. 131
Spiral wrapping of Irregular Shaped Process Equipment.

When equipment must be frequently removed for servicing, the loop method of spiral wrapping is recommended as illustrated below.

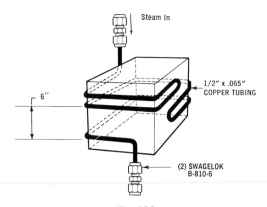

Fig. 132
Spiral Loop Wrapping of Process Equipment for Easy Removal.

Flat Grid Method: For flat or irregular surfaces, ¼″ O.D. tracer tubing should be used. The tubing should be bent to form a grid and shaped to the surface. A 6″ spacing should be maintained between coils as illustrated in Fig. 133.

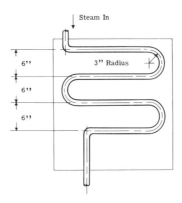

Steam In

6''   3'' Radius

6''

6''

Fig. 133
Flat Grid Method of Tracing Process Equipment.

STEAM TRAP INSTALLATION

A typical tracer line steam trap installation is shown in Fig. 135. The efficiency of tracer systems depends a great deal on the proper installation of steam traps. It is recommended that the following guide rules be used:

1. Provide a 1 ft. offset in the tracer line approximately 2 ft. from the vertical run to the trap. This offset will collect condensate and help in steam separation.

2. Insulate the steam tracer line to within 2 lineal ft. of the trap inlet.

3. Always install a strainer in front of the trap to protect the steam trap seating surfaces.

4. Install a section of ½ " tubing by 6" long to provide a dirt trap in front of the strainer. Large pieces of dirt or contamination accumulate in the dirt trap, thus increasing the service life of the strainer.

5. Install the trap, control valves, and strainer as close to the ground as practical.

6. Use ½ " O.D. tubing for the trap discharge line. This line should be as short as possible and pointed down toward the ground. Discharge into a drain or sewer when one is convenient. Make sure the discharge line is not a safety hazard.

7. Provide proper support for wiring the horizontal discharge line and accessories.

8. Suggested arrangement of components is shown in Fig. 135.

Fig. 134
Snoop Liquid Leak Detectors

SYSTEM START-UP INSTRUCTIONS

All new tracer lines should be pressurized with air and checked for leaks with SNOOP® or REAL COOL SNOOP® Leak Detectors. After performing any needed repairs, the system is ready for start-up with steam.

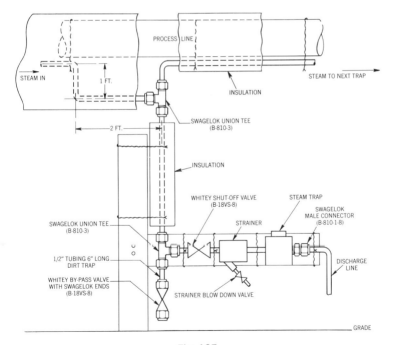

Fig. 135

SUGGESTED STEAM TRAP INSTALLATION
ON A TRACER LINE.

The following procedure should be followed: (see Fig. 135.)

1. Open the WHITEY by-pass valves and close the WHITEY shut-off valves.

2. Admit steam to the system. Leave the by-pass valves open until a free flow of steam is obtained. The blow-down will heat the system quickly and remove any dirt or accumulated contamination.

3. Shut the by-pass valves and open the shut-off valves. Now, the full system is in operation. Check visually for steam flow at discharge line.

4. Open the strainer blowdown valve, remove dirt, and close the valve.

5. All traps should be inspected for proper operation. A trap that is leaking will blow steam continuously while one working properly, under normal conditions, will operate intermittently. Leaking traps can normally be repaired by disassembling and cleaning the seating surfaces.

REVIEW THESE CONSIDERATIONS BEFORE
SELECTING A TRACING METHOD

The capability of any given tracing installation must be matched carefully with the requirements of the system to be traced. Here are some important factors to consider:

Extreme care should be used on installations where difficult bends and complicated valve manifolds are encountered.

Choice of tracing techniques can be narrowed by temperature requirements, particularly where high temperatures are needed or where temperatures must be held within precise limits.

Length and diameter of the process piping to be traced provide an indication of the liquid volume to be maintained at a specified temperature. Therefore, these dimensions should be measured accurately to help estimate tracing system heat requirements.

Heat loss depends to a large degree on the location of the piping to be traced. For example, different tracing methods would be needed for two identical installations if one were outdoors in a cold environment and the other were indoors. Another pertinent factor in estimating heat loss is the type and thickness of the insulation that covers the pipe and tracing.

Choice of tracing techniques is limited if the installation is an existing process pipe that may not be moved or disconnected. New installations seldom present this problem.

Some methods will be ruled out if hot spots on a pipe would be incompatible with the process to be traced (causing unsafe conditions, for instance). Special installation may be needed.

Heat source for the tracing system must be constant. Steam, for example, must be available even during shutdown. Electric power should be sufficient to prevent power failure due to overloading.

DOWTHERM "A" FLUID

Dowtherm "A" fluid is a temperature maintaining fluid, used like steam but at a higher temperature for condensing vapor, i. e., 60 psig instead of 650 psig, and for temperatures up to 700° F.

In manufacturing, Dowtherm "A" fluid is a clear liquid which darkens rapidly on use. On installations protected from the weather, it can be used without steam tracing. Its freezing point is 53.6° F. and it boils at an atmospheric point of 494.8° F.

The flash point of Dowtherm "A" fluid is 255° F., but it also has a relatively higher fire point at 275° F.

DOWTHERM "E" FLUID

Dowtherm "E" fluid with a boiling point of 350° F. was developed to fill the gap between steam at 100 psig and Dowtherm "A" fluid at atmospheric pressure. It is recommended for use in vapor phase systems in temperatures below 500° F.

In general, carbon steel, stainless steel, aluminum and Monel are acceptable for use with Dowtherm fluid. For specific uses, a thorough engineering analysis should be made. Bellows valves, as manufactured by the NUPRO Company have been used successfully with both types of Dowtherm fluid.

LIQUID SODIUM

Introduction

The properties of liquid sodium are a study in themselves, and the purpose of it in this manual is for general information only.

As steam and Dowtherm fluids are used to control other fluids at temperatures up to 750° F., liquid sodium is being used at much higher temperatures. In all three media (Dowtherm "A" fluid, Dowtherm "E" fluid, Liquid Sodium), the objective is to maintain temperature control in an economical manner. Sodium is one of the alkali metals produced cheaply and in large quantities .

The heat-transfer coefficient of liquid sodium is among the highest known. It is an element and therefore does not decompose, polymerize or carbonize. Oxygen reacts to form oxides, which become factors in corrosion.

Handling liquid sodium presents other problems due to the extreme reactivity of sodium with oxygen and moisture. Spontaneous ignition is, of course, the most common danger. Quick action should be taken to cool the sodium and to prevent access to air. Dry soda ash or salt are usually sufficient to extinguish a fire. While it is true that sodium possesses many of the properties which make it hazardous for certain applications, proper precautions permit its safe use even at high temperatures and pressures. Care should be taken in progressively heating liquid sodium, particularly from either the solid-liquid or solid-gas interface installation to prevent cold spots and contamination.

The latest and most widely accepted application for liquid sodium is as a nuclear reactor coolant. Many existing nuclear test facilities are presently using this coolant media, and it may well be the coolant of the future for the nuclear age.

VACUUM SYSTEMS

SWAGELOK Tube Fittings are widely used on critical vacuum applications. The importance of keeping all action moving in an axial direction with absolutely no torque or rotary motion in making a seal is demonstrated in applying SWAGELOK Tube Fittings to vacuum work. Any scoring of the sealing surfaces would prevent a helium tight seal. The axial motion when making and remaking joints with SWAGELOK Tube Fittings results in pressing the sealing surfaces together, so that there is no scoring of any surfaces and, therefore, helium tight joints can be made over and over again. Extreme care should be used in the handling of tubing for vacuum service, to insure successful use in your system.

In vacuum work, cleanliness is absolutely essential. All tubing used should be degreased and then dried thoroughly. If this is not done, oils and moisture will vaporize as pressure is reduced and the system will appear to leak even though it is tight. The tube fittings for vacuum work should also be degreased. When using stainless steel or other special alloys that have tendencies to gall, it is recommended that only the body and front ferrule be degreased as these are the only items that are within the system. The nut and rear ferrule are outside the sealed system and special lubricants that have been applied to prevent galling should not be removed.

If a vacuum connection will be frequently disconnected, it has been found particularly efficient to use a TFE front ferrule with a metal SWAGELOK Tube Fitting and a metal back ferrule. Consideration should be given to the cold-flow properties of TFE. Such a connection can be used very effectively when connecting devices to a helium leak detector for testing. CAJON Company markets a complete product line designed for vacuum systems, under the trade names of Ultra-Torr and VCO & VCR connectors. Both SWAGELOK Tube Fittings and CAJON Fittings can be used on all vacuum systems. Caution should be used if fitting components contain elastomers, especially if the vacuum system will see temperatures in the bakeout range.

In bakeout applications, one should not mix metals when system temperatures will be increased unless coefficients of expansion are considered. For example, if a stainless steel type 316 fitting (coefficient of expansion 11 x 10^{-6}/in/in/°F) was installed on Monel tubing (co-efficient of expansion 7.8 x 10^{-6}/in/in/°F), when the temperature is raised, the stainless steel increases in size at a greater rate than the tubing. This has the effect of the fitting becoming loose on the tubing because of a property of the material (coefficient of expansion) coupled with the temperature change. On the other hand, if Monel is put on stainless and raised to a high temperature, the joint becomes tighter. However, the stainless steel tubing increasing in size at a greater rate than the Monel fitting may yield the fitting and a leak could result upon return-ing to lower temperatures. Mixing materials is not recommended, i.e., using different materials for fittings and tubing, unless an engineering analysis is made of temperature variation.

For your higher temperature vacuum systems, in the bakeout range, SWAGELOK Tube Fittings have proven very successful. In meeting your requirements for more sophisticated components, CAJON Com-pany offers a complete range of vacuum products.

For convenience, coefficients of expansion for materials commonly employed in tube fitting applications are given below:

	Coefficient of Expansion in./in./° F.
Stainless Steel (304 and 316)	9.00 to 11 x 10^{-6}
Monel	7.80 x 10^{-6}
Brass	11.40 x 10^{-6}
Aluminum	13.00 to 14 x 10^{-6}
Carbon Steel	8.40 x 10^{-6}
Copper	9.80 x 10^{-6}

Temperature rating: Operating temperature ratings are dependent on application and installation methods, cycle life required and other variables. Consult your local distributor for additional information.

Use STRIP-TEEZE TFE tape on pipe threads in a vacuum system to create a seal. VAC-GOOP lubricant is recommended to be used on bolts and surfaces where it is desired to prevent galling.

CAJON® VACUUM PRODUCTS

Due to advances in technology and the increased use of vacuum systems in both research and industry, the vacuum field has become highly specialized. In order to properly service this field the CAJON Vacuum Products line has been developed. With a wide range of products CAJON can supply components for the most basic to highly sophisticated vacuum systems.

The following will provide technical as well as general application information on each CAJON Vacuum Product.

ULTRA-TORR® FITTINGS

PURPOSE

CAJON Ultra-Torr Fittings are designed to provide a vacuum-tight seal with quick, finger-tight assembly and reusability on glass, metal or plastic tubing.

APPLICATIONS

CAJON Ultra-Torr Fittings can be used on all vacuum systems except where bake-out temperatures would damage the O-Ring. Ultra-Torr Fittings can also be used on any system utilizing glass, metal or plastic tubing.

FEATURES

• Helium leak-tight seal for use on low, medium and high vacuum service • Reusable without changing fitting components • Perfect alignment of O-Ring, sleeve and nut for positive sealing and easy assembly • Can be used on any system utilizing glass, metal, or plastic tubing • Finger-tight assembly and disassembly without distortion of tubing • Can be used with tubing O.D. as much as $\frac{1}{32}''$ under-size • Ideal for use with millimeter tubing (such as glass) where the O.D. may vary • Can be used on all vacuum applications except where bake-out temperatures would damage the O-Ring • Variety of shapes include unions, adapters, connectors, elbows, tees, crosses, etc. • Furnished in sizes from $\frac{1}{16}''$ to 2 inches • Standard materials are brass and 316 stainless steel•Ultra-Torr Fittings can be provided in many other metals and plastics • One-piece forgings used on tees, elbows, crosses, etc.

TECHNICAL DATA

Materials: Body — Brass and type 316 stainless steel as standard.

O-Ring — 70 Durometer Viton as standard. Other materials and hardnesses on request through your local distributor.

All Other Parts — Same material as the body.

Temperature Rating: Maximum Temperature rating using a Viton O-Ring is 232°C (450°F).

Pressure Ratings: CAJON Ultra-Torr Fittings have been specifically designed for use on low, medium and high vacuum service. They have also been used in some pressurized systems by mechanically containing the tubing to prevent the tubing from being forced from the fitting.

Sealants: For efficient seal performance in vacuum applications, the Ultra-Torr O-Ring is wetted with a very thin film of silicone vacuum grease. Replacement O-Rings should be wetted with lubricants or sealants compatible with the system.

Testing: CAJON Ultra-Torr Fittings with finger-tight assembly have been consistently helium leak-tested to a rate of 0.0004 M.C.F.H. or 4.14 x 10^{-9} atm. cc/sec. without leakage.

ULTRA-TORR ADAPTER

Sample Part No.

SS	-	4	-	UT	-	A	-	4

316 Stainless Steel — ¼″ Tube OD — Ultra Torr — Adapter — ¼″ Tube Stub

ULTRA-TORR BORE-THROUGH ADAPTER

Sample Part No.

B	-	2	-	UT	-	A	-	4BT

Brass — ⅛″ Tube OD — Ultra Torr — Adapter — ¼″ Bored Through Tube Stub

ULTRA-TORR MALE CONNECTOR

Sample Part No.

SS	-	8	-	UT	-	1	-	8

316 Stainless Steel — ½″ Tube OD — Ultra Torr — Male Connector — ½″ MPT

ULTRA-TORR UNION

Sample Part No.

SS	-	16	-	UT	-	6
316 Stainless Steel		1″ Tube OD		Ultra Torr		Union

ULTRA-TORR TEE

Sample Part No.

B	-	6	-	UT	-	3
Brass		3/8″ Tube OD		Ultra Torr		Tee

VCO® O-RING VACUUM COUPLINGS

PURPOSE

The CAJON VCO Coupling is designed for rapid make-up in low, medium and high vacuum applications as well as positive pressure applications.

The CAJON VCO Coupling design allows repositioning of components through 360 degrees. No axial clearance is required for component removal or repositioning.

BENEFITS OF COMPONENT STOCK

CAJON VCO Coupling parts are stocked as separate items to allow the user maximum convenience and flexibility in making up a system or connecting a component. Common parts, such as the nut and gland can be purchased in larger quantities at lower cost. Inventories can be greatly reduced by eliminating the duplication of these common parts. Each body style can be combined with a gland and nut of the same size to make up the required coupling. Sizes are designated by the first digit of the catalog number. The standard Viton O-Ring is always included with the body.

APPLICATIONS

Vacuum and pressure systems • Pump port connections • Auxiliary ports • Sampling lines • Valve port connections • Portable equipment coupling • Transfer line connections • Used in brazed or welded systems

FEATURES

No axial clearance needed for disassembly • Minimum dead space to reduce pump-down time • Cannot be over-tightened • Metal-to-metal contact contains O-Ring • Leak test port at seal to provide immediate leak detection • Precision mating parts for dependable seal • Quality thread form for repeated makeup • Available in high strength forged tees, elbows and crosses • Standard O-Rings can be used for replacement • Various end connections available from 1/8″ through 1″ • Low customer inventories through separate component stock.

TECHNICAL DATA

Materials: Body, Gland, Nut — Brass or 316 stainless steel as standard.

O-Ring — 70 Durometer Viton as standard. Other materials and hardnesses on request from your local distributor.

Temperature Ratings: Maximum temperature rating using a Viton O-Ring is 232°C (450°F).

Pressure Ratings: Pressure ratings for each component are calculated in accordance with power piping code per A.N.S.I. B31.3 paragraph 304.1.2. Allowable working pressures listed include a safety factor of four (4:1).

Sealants: For efficient performance, the VCO O-Ring is wetted with a very thin film of silicone vacuum grease. Replacement O-Rings should be wetted with lubricants or sealants compatible with the system.

Testing: CAJON VCO Couplings have been consistently helium leak tested to a rate of 0.0004 M.C.F.H. or 4.14 x 10^{-9} atm. cc/sec. without leakage.

INSTALLATION INSTRUCTIONS

When soldering, brazing or welding is performed on the body end of the coupling, the O-Ring should be removed to prevent damage.

The coupling should be tightened no less than 1/8 turn past finger-tight to assure metal-to-metal contact for both vacuum and pressure applications.

NO AXIAL CLEARANCE NEEDED FOR DISASSEMBLY

The coupling can be disconnected and a section removed from the system without disturbing other components or connections.

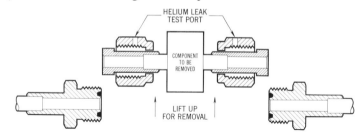

VCO COMMON PARTS

VCO NUT

Sample Part No.

SS	-	4	-	VCO	-	4
316 Stainless Steel		¼″ Tube OD		VCO		Nut

VCO GLAND

Sample Part No.

B	-	8	-	VCO	-	3
Brass		½″ Tube OD		VCO		Gland

VCO BODIES

VCO BODY

Sample Part No.

SS	-	2	-	VCO	-	1
316 Stainless Steel		⅛″ Tube OD		VCO		Socket Weld Male End

MALE CONNECTOR BODY

Sample Part No.

B	-	16	-	VCO	-	1	-	16

Brass   1″   VCO   Male   1″
      Tube   Connector   Male
      OD   Pipe
                                     Thread

FEMALE CONNECTOR BODY

Sample Part No.

B	-	12	-	VCO	-	7	-	12

Brass   ¾″   VCO   Female   ¾″
      Tube   Connector   Female
      OD   Pipe
                                     Thread

VCO TO SWAGELOK CONNECTOR BODY

Sample Part No.

SS	-	4	-	VCO	-	6	-	400

316   ¼″   VCO   Union   ¼″ O.D.
Stainless   Tube   SWAGELOK
Steel   OD   Tube End

ELBOW BODY

Sample Part No.

B	-	10	-	VCO	-	9

Brass   ⅝″   VCO   Elbow
      Tube
      OD

TEE BODY

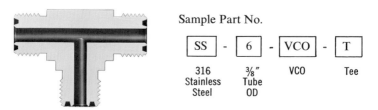

Sample Part No.

| SS | - | 6 | - | VCO | - | T |

316
Stainless
Steel

3/8"
Tube
OD

VCO

Tee

VCR® VACUUM COUPLINGS

PURPOSE

CAJON VCR Couplings allow component removal or repositioning without the need for axial clearance. When space is at a premium, VCR components greatly simplify system layout and installation.

This versatile design is suitable for ultra-high vacuum applications as well as high pressure systems. All metal seals permit VCR Couplings to be used with low or high operating temperatures. Helium leak-tight systems can be rapidly assembled or disassembled and components can be reused many times.

BENEFITS OF COMPONENT STOCK

CAJON VCR Coupling parts are stocked as separate items to allow the users maximum confidence and flexibility in making up a system or connecting a component. Common parts, such as the nuts, glands and gaskets, can be purchased in larger quantities at lower cost. Inventories can be greatly reduced by eliminating the duplication of common parts necessary for assembled stocks. The various bodies can be combined with nuts, glands and gaskets of the same size to make up many different combinations of assembled couplings. Sizes are designated by the first digit of the part number.

APPLICATIONS

Industrial and research vacuum systems • Low and high pressure systems • Pump port connections • Valve port connections • Auxiliary ports • Sampling systems • Transfer line connection • Steam lines • Refrigeration lines • Corrosive fluid lines • Cylinder connections •

Cryogenics • High temperature applications • Used in brazed or welded systems.

FEATURES

Practically no axial clearance needed for disassembly • Gasket position eliminates virtual leaks and allows fast pump-down • Test port at seal provides for immediate positive leak testing • Mirror finished sealing surface for positive, repetitive seals • Lapped gasket surfaces for minimum torque make-up and helium leak-tight sealing • Variety of gasket materials • Contained seal for safety in pressurized systems • Quality thread form for repeated make-up • Precision mating parts for dependable seal • Plated threads for repeated make-up • Available in high strength forged tees, elbows and crosses • Various end connections available in sizes from $\frac{1}{16}''$ through $1''$ • Low inventories through separate component stock.

INSTALLATION INSTRUCTIONS

The Coupling should be tightened no less than $\frac{1}{8}$ turn past finger-tight for stainless steel and nickel gaskets, and $\frac{1}{4}$ turn past finger-tight for OFHC copper, aluminum and TFE gaskets.

NO AXIAL CLEARANCE NEEDED FOR DISASSEMBLY

The VCR Couplings can be disconnected and a section removed from the system without disturbing other components or connections.

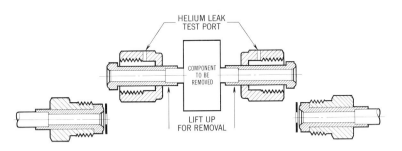

TECHNICAL DATA

Materials: Bodies, Female Nuts, Glands, Male Nuts — 316 stainless steel.

Gaskets — Nickel is standard. Type 316 stainless steel, OFHC copper, TFE and aluminum are available on request.

Temperature Ratings: Maximum temperature ratings for VCR 316 stainless steel couplings are based on the gasket material used as follows:

Aluminum	343°C (650°F)
Nickel	593°C (1100°F)
OFHC Copper	371°C (700°F)
Stainless Steel	537°C (1000°F)
TFE	232°C (450°F)

Pressure Ratings: Pressure ratings for each component are calculated in accordance with power piping code per A.N.S.I. B31.3 paragraph 304.1.2. All pressure ratings listed are for 316 stainless steel components with nickel gaskets at room temperature and include a safety factor of four (4:1).

Testing: CAJON VCR Couplings have been consistently helium leak tested at a rate of 0.0004 M.C.F.H. or 4.14×10^{-9} atm. cc/sec. without detectable leakage.

VCR COMMON PARTS

FEMALE NUT

Sample Part No.

$\boxed{\text{SS}}$ - $\boxed{4}$ - $\boxed{\text{VCR}}$ - $\boxed{1}$

316 Stainless Steel   ¼" Tube OD   VCR   Female Nut

GASKET

Sample Part No.

$\boxed{\text{Ni}}$ - $\boxed{2}$ - $\boxed{\text{VCR}}$ - $\boxed{2}$

Nickel   ⅛" Tube OD   VCR   Gasket

GLAND

Sample Part No.

$\boxed{\text{SS}}$ - $\boxed{8}$ - $\boxed{\text{VCR}}$ - $\boxed{3}$

316 Stainless Steel   ½" Tube OD   VCR   Gland

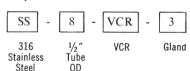

MALE WELD GLAND

Sample Part No.

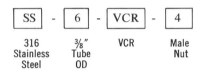

| SS | - | 10 | - | VCR | - | (10MW) | - | 3 |

316
Stainless
Steel

⅝″
Tube
OD

VCR

⅝″
Male
Weld

Gland

MALE NUT

Sample Part No.

| SS | - | 6 | - | VCR | - | 4 |

316
Stainless
Steel

⅜″
Tube
OD

VCR

Male
Nut

VCR BODIES

MALE CONNECTOR BODY

Sample Part No.

| SS | - | 4 | - | VCR | - | 1 | - | 4 |

316
Stainless
Steel

¼″
Tube
OD

VCR

Male
Con-
nector

¼″ Male
Pipe
Thread

FEMALE CONNECTOR BODY

Sample Part No.

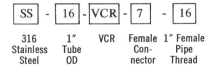

| SS | - | 16 | - | VCR | - | 7 | - | 16 |

316
Stainless
Steel

1″
Tube
OD

VCR

Female
Con-
nector

1″ Female
Pipe
Thread

TEE BODY

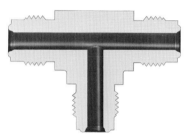

Sample Part No.

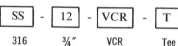

| SS | - | 12 | - | VCR | - | T |

| 316 Stainless Steel | ¾″ Tube OD | VCR | Tee |

CROSS BODY

Sample Part No.

| SS | - | 8 | - | VCR | - | CS |

| 316 Stainless Steel | ½″ Tube OD | VCR | Cross |

ELBOW BODY

Sample Part No.

| SS | - | 1 | - | VCR | - | 9 |

| 316 Stainless Steel | 1/16″ Tube OD | VCR | Elbow |

DOUBLE MALE UNION BODY

Sample Part No.

| SS | - | 6 | - | VCR | - | 6DM |

| 316 Stainless Steel | ⅜″ Tube OD | VCR | Double Male Union |

DOUBLE FEMALE UNION BODY

Sample Part No.

SS	-	2	-	VCR	-	6DF

316 Stainless Steel	⅛" Tube OD	VCR	Double Female Union

FLEXIBLE STAINLESS STEEL TUBING

PURPOSE

CAJON Flexible Stainless Steel Tubing is the ideal replacement for rubber, plastic and glass tubing in high vacuum applications.

APPLICATIONS

Vibration absorbers • Relief for thermal expansion • Low pressure, high purity systems • Industrial and research vacuum applications • Replace expensive vacuum fittings • Adjustable-length static metal seal • Excellent as a heat transfer device • Permits connection of misaligned components.

FEATURES

The extremely flexible nature of CAJON Flexible Stainless Steel Tubing provides compensation for misalignment, expansion and contraction in fabricated systems. CAJON Flexible Tubing is compressible by at least 20% and extendable by 50% of its nominal produced flexible length.

TECHNICAL DATA

Material: 321 stainless steel.

Temperature Rating: Operating temperature ratings are dependent on application and installation methods, cycle life required, O.D. and nominal length of tubing, angular displacement and other variables. Contact your local distributor for additional information.

Pressure Rating: Ultra-High Vacuum to 25 psig.

Sample Part No.

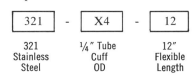

| 321 | - | X4 | - | 12 |

| 321 Stainless Steel | 1/4" Tube Cuff OD | 12" Flexible Length |

FLEXIBLE STAINLESS STEEL TUBING ACCESSORIES

BRAZE ADAPTER AND SWAGELOK ADAPTER

Provides length of standard tubing on the end of the flexible tube.

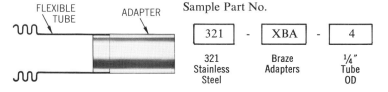

Sample Part No.

| 321 | - | XBA | - | 4 |

| 321 Stainless Steel | Braze Adapters | 1/4" Tube OD |

Brazing should be done in a dry Hydrogen atmosphere or vacuum.

O-RING ADAPTER

Supports Flexible Tube Cuff.

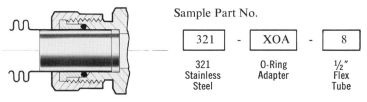

Sample Part No.

| 321 | - | XOA | - | 8 |

| 321 Stainless Steel | O-Ring Adapter | 1/2" Flex Tube |

WELD RINGS

Protects the Tube Cuff from warping during welding.

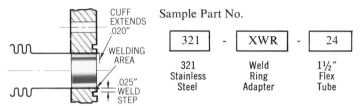

CUFF EXTENDS .020"

WELDING AREA

.025"

WELD STEP

Sample Part No.

| 321 | - | XWR | - | 24 |

| 321 Stainless Steel | Weld Ring Adapter | 1½" Flex Tube |

T.I.G. welding should always be used.

FLEXIBLE GLASS-END TUBING

PURPOSE

CAJON Flexible Glass-end Tubing is designed to isolate vibration from glass systems.

APPLICATIONS

Vibration absorbers • Relief for thermal expansion • Low pressure, high purity systems • Industrial and research vacuum systems • Replace expensive vacuum fittings • Permits connection of misaligned components.

FEATURES

CAJON Flexible Glass-end Tubing compensates for expansion, misalignment and vibration in glass systems. The one step glass-to-stainless transition utilizes only the parent materials. No overlapping seams to entrap gases. The nominal produced flexible length is compressible by at least 20% and extendable by 50%.

CAJON Flexible Tubing is available with glass on both ends or on one end for glass-to-metal transitions. The glass end is flame cut for smooth edges. Glass ends are stress relieved.

TECHNICAL DATA

Material: 321 stainless steel fused to type 7740 Pyrex glass tube.

Temperature Rating: Operating temperature ratings are dependent on application and installation methods, cycle life required, O.D. and nominal length of tubing, angular displacement and other variables. Contact your local distributor for additional information.

Pressure Rating: Ultra-high vacuum to 25 psig.

GLASS BOTH ENDS

Sample Part No.

G321	-	4	-	2

Glass to 321 Stainless Steel	¼″ Flex Tube	2″ Flexible Length

GLASS ONE END

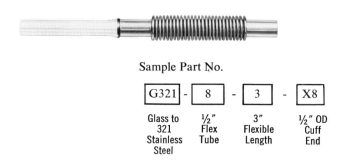

Sample Part No.

G321	-	8	-	3	-	X8

Glass to 321 Stainless Steel	½″ Flex Tube	3″ Flexible Length	½″ OD Cuff End

GLASS/METAL TRANSITION TUBES

PURPOSE

CAJON Glass/Metal Transition Tubes are designed for converting from a glass to a metal system through a transition which utilizes only the parent materials.

APPLICATIONS

Transition from a glass system to a metal system • Industrial and research vacuum systems • Corrosive fluid lines • Connect ionization gauges to stainless steel vacuum systems • Either end adaptable to CAJON Ultra-Torr Fittings • Stainless steel end adaptable to SWAGE-

LOK Tube Fitting • Connecting valves to glass systems • Sight gauges • Manometers • Low pressure, high purity systems • High temperature applications.

FEATURES

One step glass-to-stainless transition eliminates troublesome graded seals • Smooth internal surface for high conductance • No overlapping seams to entrap gases • Nonporous transition area to prevent absorption and outgassing • Transition structure stronger than parent glass • Transition area offers thermal compatibility with parent materials • Glass end is flame cut for smooth edges • Glass ends are stress relieved.

TECHNICAL DATA

Material: Glass Tube — 7740 Pyrex. Metal Tube — 304 stainless steel.

Temperature Rating: Temperatures are limited to the strain point of the glass end which is 515°C (959°F).

Pressure Limits: Ultra-high vacuum to 25 psig.

Testing: All CAJON Glass/Metal Transition Tubes are 100% stress relieved, and leak tested before leaving the factory.

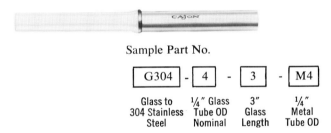

Sample Part No.

G304	-	4	-	3	-	M4
Glass to 304 Stainless Steel		1/4" Glass Tube OD Nominal		3" Glass Length		1/4" Metal Tube OD

VACUUM BUTT WELD FITTINGS

PURPOSE

CAJON Vacuum Butt Weld Fittings are designed to provide light weight, high conductance connections for vacuum and positive pressure systems.

APPLICATIONS

Industrial and research vacuum systems • Vacuum coating and plating equipment • High purity gases • Cryogenics • High temperature applications • Vacuum instruments • Environmental testing • Positive pressure systems • Tubular heating and cooling lines using 180° tube bends • Refrigeration lines • Manifold branches • Tees and crosses are adaptable to CAJON Socket Weld Gland Ends and Socket Weld Fittings • All configurations are adaptable to: • CAJON Flanges (rotatable and non-rotatable) • CAJON Flexible Tubing — (use braze adapter)

• CAJON Glass/Metal Transition Tubes • CAJON VCO and VCR Weld Glands • CAJON Butt Weld Fittings.

FEATURES

Lightweight, butt weld fittings to avoid virtual leaks • Smooth, controlled internal finish for maximum conductance and minimum condensation or absorption of gases • 316 stainless steel to prevent absorption and outgassing • Uniform wall for good weld consistency • Rigid tolerance control for ease of fabrication alignment • Uniform branch lengths in each size • Available in crosses, tees, caps, 45° and 90° elbows and 180° bends in a variety of tube sizes • Caps are designed for easy drilling to be used as reducer couplings • Crosses and tees to ¾ " are machined from forgings — no production welds • All CAJON Vacuum Butt Weld Fittings are electro-polished.

TECHNICAL DATA

Materials: Crosses, Tees — 316 stainless steel forgings. 45° and 90° Elbows, and 180° Bends — 316 stainless steel seamless tubing.

Caps — 316 stainless steel bar stock. All material listed has a .05% carbon content maximum.

Pressure Ratings: Pressures listed are calculated in accordance with power piping code per A.N.S.I. B31.3 paragraph 304.1.2.

Fitting Size (T)	Allowable Working Pressure PSIG
1/4"	5,600
3/8"	3,600
1/2"	3,800
3/4"	3,000

Allowable working pressures listed include a safety factor of four (4:1).

BUTT WELD TEE

Sample Part No.

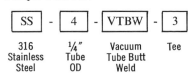

| SS | - | 4 | - | VTBW | - | 3 |

316 Stainless Steel   ¼" Tube OD   Vacuum Tube Butt Weld   Tee

BUTT WELD CROSS

Sample Part No.

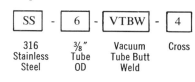

| SS | - | 6 | - | VTBW | - | 4 |

316
Stainless
Steel

3/8"
Tube
OD

Vacuum
Tube Butt
Weld

Cross

BUTT WELD 90° ELBOW

Sample Part No.

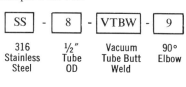

| SS | - | 8 | - | VTBW | - | 9 |

316
Stainless
Steel

1/2"
Tube
OD

Vacuum
Tube Butt
Weld

90°
Elbow

BUTT WELD 45° ELBOW

Sample Part No.

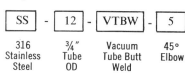

| SS | - | 12 | - | VTBW | - | 5 |

316
Stainless
Steel

3/4"
Tube
OD

Vacuum
Tube Butt
Weld

45°
Elbow

BUTT WELD 180° BEND

Sample Part No.

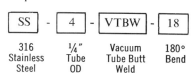

| SS | - | 4 | - | VTBW | - | 18 |

316
Stainless
Steel

1/4"
Tube
OD

Vacuum
Tube Butt
Weld

180°
Bend

BUTT WELD CAP

Sample Part No.

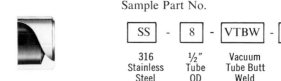

SS	-	8	-	VTBW	-	CP
316 Stainless Steel		½" Tube OD		Vacuum Tube Butt Weld		Cap

VACUUM FLANGES

PURPOSE

CAJON Vacuum Flanges provide single-seal reliability for ultra-high vacuum systems using tubing up to 1½ inches outside diameter. This unique all metal sealing principle provides consistent performance at high or low temperatures in vacuum or positive pressure applications. No axial clearance is required for removing or re-installing system components.

CAJON CF Vacuum Flanges are designed for use as a non-rotatable unit to hold the tubing or components in a fixed relationship.

CAJON CFR Vacuum Flanges are rotatable units made up of an insert and clamping ring that allow for alignment of system components. Realignment or repositioning of components such as valves and pumps can also be accomplished.

APPLICATIONS

Industrial and research vacuum systems • Pump and valve port connections • Auxiliary ports • Vacuum test chamber ports • Mass spectrometers, gas analyzers, particle accelerators • Space and environmental test equipment • Epitaxial reactors, thin film evaporators, semiconductor equipment • Refrigeration lines • Corrosive fluid lines • Cryogenics • High temperature applications • Used in brazed or welded systems.

FEATURES

A unique double toroid design results in double gripping on the face of the gasket • The inner toroid provides a single positive vacuum seal • The outer toroid provides seal compression which improves vibration resistance and thermal cycling capabilities • Positive vent to atmosphere between inner and outer toroids avoids virtual leaks sometimes caused by double sealing • Lapped gasket and flange sealing surfaces lower the bolt torque required for a positive vacuum seal • Seal area protected from damage during handling and installation by a projecting ridge • The gasket O.D. is guided during assembly by the projecting ridge • Flange to flange make-up for a visual check of proper assembly — no torque reading required • Combination helium test port and axial wedge slot • Stress-relief groove at tube weld area • Lubricated bolts to reduce torque and prevent galling during assembly • 12 point bolts for maximum wrench positioning and swing • CAJON Flanges can be used with other types of flanges on existing equipment • Assembly, disassembly and welding instructions are shown on a card included with each flange.

SEALING PRINCIPLE

The CAJON Flange makes a positive vacuum seal through a unique geometry which retains high compressive pressures upon its sealing surface. A quad toroid arrangement grips the gasket face and places a portion of the gasket under biaxial compression (C). This design eliminates the need for vertical wall containment of the gasket O.D. All sealing pressures acting upon the gasket are controlled by the high tensile clamping bolts.

Expansion and contraction caused by thermal cycling are limited at the seal by placing the gasket in compression with a single member. The quad toroid arrangement contains the gasket to prevent loss of seal at high temperatures.

A positive vacuum seal is effected at the inner toroid (A). A groove between (A) and (B) provides a positive vent to atmosphere. The outer toroid (B), which is vented to prevent double sealing, provides seal compression which improves vibration resistance, and thermal cycling capabilities.

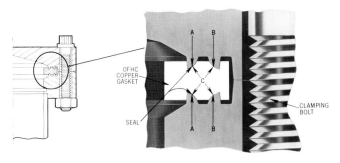

TECHNICAL DATA

Materials: Flange Clamp Rings, Flange Inserts and Non-Rotatable Flanges — 304L stainless steel. Bolts — A286 high strength alloy steel. Nuts — Silver plated 316 stainless steel. Gaskets — OFHC Copper, Viton or Nickel.

Temperature Ratings: Maximum Temperature Ratings are based on the gasket material used, as follows:

OFHC Copper Gasket	500°C (932°F)
Viton Gasket	232°C (450°F)
Nickel Gasket	537°C (1,000°F)

Pressure Rating: Ultra-high Vacuum to 2500 psig.

Testing: CAJON CF and CFR Flanges have been consistently helium leak tested to a rate of .0004 M.C.F.H. or 4.14 x 10^{-9} atm. cc/sec. without detectable leakage.

Sample Part Nos.

304L	-	24CF	-	275

304L
Stainless
Steel

1½" Tube
OD (Non-
Rotatable)

2¾"
OD
Flange

304L	-	24CFR	-	275

304L
Stainless
Steel

1½" Tube
OD
(Rotatable)

2¾"
OD
Flange

Sample Part Nos.

304L	-	24CF	-	275	-	(Blind)

304L
Stainless
Steel

1½" Max.
Tube OD (Non-
Rotatable)

2¾"
OD
Flange

Blind

304L	-	24CFR	-	275	-	(Blind)

304L
Stainless
Steel

1½" Max.
Tube OD
(Rotatable)

2¾"
OD
Flange

Blind

ACCESSORIES FOR CAJON CF AND CFR VACUUM FLANGES

We recommend CAJON Gaskets and Bolts be used with CAJON Vacuum Flanges for maximum reliability. Metal gaskets are lapped for positive vacuum sealing. Viton gaskets are properly dimensioned for easy sealing with CAJON Vacuum Flanges. The 12 point bolts permit ease of assembly using standard 12 point socket or box end wrenches. The lubrication helps prevent galling on assembly or disassembly, especially with high temperatures. Make-up torque is reduced considerably. For strength and temperature compatibility, nuts are made of high tensile, silver plated 316 stainless steel, and the lubricated bolts are of Alloy A286.

Description	Part Number	
Copper gasket	CU-CF-275-2 (OFHC)	
Viton gasket	VITON-CF-275-2	
Nickel gasket	Ni-CF-275-2	
¼-28x1¼" long Alloy A286 lubricated bolt (12 point) with plated 316 SS nut	A286-¼-28x1¼" (12 pt.)	BOLT—requires ¼" standard 12 point socket or box end wrench NUT—⁷⁄₁₆" hex flat

GENERAL INFORMATION

The numbering system for all CAJON Products is designed so that all part numbers are prefixed by a MATERIAL DESIGNATOR code followed by a dash. Examples: B - (brass), SS - (316 stainless steel), etc.

PRESSURE CONVERSION TABLE

From \ To	Atm.	in. Hg	in H₂O	Microns	mm. Hg	PSIA	Torr
Atm.	1	29.92	406.8	760,000	760	14.7	760
in. Hg	.03342	1	13.60	25,400	25.40	.4912	25.40
in. H₂O	.00246	.07355	1	1,868.3	1.868	.03613	1.868
Microns	.00000132	.00003937	.000535	1	.001	.00001934	.001
mm. Hg	.00132	.03937	.5353	1,000	1	.01934	1
PSIA	.06805	2.036	27.67	51,715	51.71	1	51.71
Torr	.00132	.03937	.5353	1,000	1	.01934	1

EXAMPLES

(1) Change FROM 25 microns vacuum TO torr units: 25 microns x .001 $\frac{torr}{micron}$ = .025 torr.

(2) Change FROM .025 torr TO in. Hg: .025 torr x .03937 $\frac{in.\ Hg}{torr}$ = .0009842 in. Hg.

(3) Change FROM .0009842 in. Hg TO mm. Hg: .0009842 in. Hg. x 25.40 $\frac{mm.\ Hg}{in.\ Hg}$ = .025 mm. Hg.

GRAPHIC SYMBOLS IN VACUUM TECHNOLOGY

The purpose of this standard is to establish a uniform system of graphic symbols in vacuum technology. ¶The graphic symbols are a shorthand method used to show graphically the functioning and inter-connections of vacuum components in a single-line schematic or flow diagram. ¶A single line diagram is one in which the graphic symbols are shown without regard to the actual physical location, size, or shape of the components. ¶A symbol shall·be considered as the aggregate of all its parts. ¶The orientation of a symbol on a drawing, including a

mirror image presentation, does not alter the meaning of the symbol.
¶A symbol may be drawn to any scale that suits a particular drawing.
¶Arrows should be omitted unless necessary for clarification. ¶Parts
from two or more symbols may be combined.

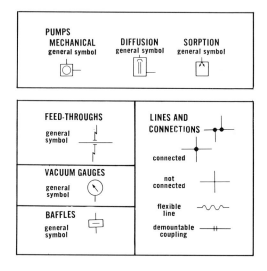

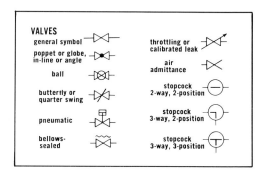

Note: This list of symbols is reprinted from the AVS Tentative Standard 7.1-1966.

CHAPTER V

TROUBLE SHOOTING

1. Tubing will not fit into fitting.

2. Fitting cannot be pulled up one and one quarter turns.

3. Leakage at pipe thread.

4. Leaks at flare joint.

5. Tubing leaks at fitting after initial installation.

6. Tubing leaks at fitting after system operation.

7. Copper tubing leaks at fitting after operation above 500° F.

8. Tubing leaks at fitting after reconnecting following maintenance.

9. Flows are too low in system.

10. Fittings cannot be disassembled after high temperature operation.

11. Tubing is deformed after system has been in operation.

12. Polyethylene tubing slips from fitting.

13. TFE tubing slips from fitting.

14. Glass tubing breaks when connecting fitting.

15. Seal is not obtained on glass tubing.

16. Tubing creeps from fitting when using plasticized PVC tubing.

TROUBLE SHOOTING

Trouble	Possible Cause	Recommended Corrective Measures
1. Tubing will not fit into fitting.	Burrs on tubing from tube cutting operation.	Deburr tubing.
	Flattened tubing from bearing too hard with hacksaw in cutting or using dull hacksaw.	Use caution in cutting soft tubing with hacksaw.
	Tubing out of round from bending improperly.	SWAGELOK Tube Fittings are manufactured to tolerances to accept the upper limit of allowed tubing diameters used in tubing manufacture. If tubing is bent too far out of round, by improper bending, the tubing will not fit into the tube fitting. Use caution with bends when near the end of tubing.
	Tubing is the wrong size for fitting. This seldom occurs but infrequently a piece of $3/8$" tubing may be used with a $5/16$" fitting by mistake.	Make sure you use the proper size fitting for each diameter tubing. Check O.D. of tubing. Determine if it is fractional or millimeter size tubing.
	Tubing is oversize. Low quality tubing may exceed the allowed tolerances for tubing.	Buy good quality tubing.

TROUBLE SHOOTING

Trouble	Possible Cause	Recommended Corrective Measures
2. Fitting cannot be pulled up proper amount of turns.	This could happen with steel or stainless steel tubing that is very hard and not intended for fluid system applications.	Buy fully annealed, hydraulic or pressure type steel and stainless tubing of recommended hardness.
	Interchange of other manufacturers components.	Use only SWAGELOK Tube Fitttings. DO NOT INTERCHANGE.
3. Leakage at Pipe Thread.	Fittings not sufficiently tightened with mating thread.	Tighten fittings.
	Experience indicates that most pipe threads make poor seals, especially on higher presssure applications.	Use GOOP — Blue, Silver, High Purity or Vac Lubricant to prevent galling. Strip Teeze TFE Tape should be used on all pipe threads to provide leak-tight sealing.
	Pipe threads damaged from galling of materials during installation.	Use GOOP — Blue, Silver, High Purity of Vac Lubricant or Strip Teeze TFE Tape should be used to prevent seizing and galling of pipe threads.
	Poor quality pipe thread either on female or male end.	Use high quality pipe threads, such as CAJON or SWAGELOK. These pipe threads are precision manufactured, but this is not sufficient to make a leak-tight connection with a pipe thread on other equipment.

TROUBLE SHOOTING

Trouble	Possible Cause	Recommended Corrective Measures
4. Leaks at Flare joint.	Poor flares.	Use SWAGELOK Tube Fittings.
	Cracked or split flare.	Use SWAGELOK Tube Fittings.
5. Tubing leaks at fitting after initial installation.	Not using SWAGELOK Tube Fittings.	Use SWAGELOK Tube Fittings.
	Fittings not pulled up properly.	Follow installation instructions. Check for hard tubing or galling. Use good quality annealed tubing.
	Tubing has deep longitudinal scratches.	Handle tubing with care. Replace tubing or cut off damaged section and reconnect.
	Fitting body was turned, instead of nut, galling seat and/or front ferrule.	Always connect fittings by turning the nut while holding body stationary.
	Fitting not tightened according to installation instructions because of inaccessible location.	Pre-swage or use Hydraulic Swaging unit, then snug. See Pre-swaging and Hydraulic swaging instructions. Page 11, Chapter 1.
	Fitting was used as vise or anchor to bend tubing by hand.	Replace tubing. Never use the fitting as a holding device for bending. This will deform the tubing inside of the fitting and pull the tube away from the seal.
	Interchange of other manufacturers' components.	Use only SWAGELOK Tube Fittings. DO NOT INTERCHANGE.

TROUBLE SHOOTING

Trouble	Possible Cause	Recommended Corrective Measures
6. Tubing leaks at fitting after system installation.	Damage caused by mechanical means outside the system.	Replace tubing and fitting and relocate where damage is less likely to be a problem.
	Corrosion is eating away fitting or tubing.	Inspect connection for corrosion. If present, check corrosion compatibility of fluid, tubing and fitting materials and ambient atmosphere. Consider galvanic action as a possible cause.
	Cracking of tubing due to over-stressing while making flare for a flare fitting.	SWAGELOK Tube Fittings should be used to replace such fittings and avoid this difficulty.
	Interchange of other manufacturers' components.	Use only SWAGELOK Tube Fittings. DO NOT INTERCHANGE.
7. Copper tubing leaks at fitting after operation above 400° F.	Copper tubing becomes very weak above 400° F. This is an inherent characteristic of the material and not a function of fitting performance. Codes limit copper tubing to 400° F.	Heavier wall copper tubing will help in some cases for temperature cycling, but in no case should copper tubing be used above 400°F. Steel or stainless tubing and fittings should be used.

TROUBLE SHOOTING

Trouble	Possible Cause	Recommended Corrective Measures
8. Tubing leaks at fitting after reconnecting following main-tenance.	Fitting not properly retightened.	Follow retightening instructions.
	Dirt got into fitting or on ferrules while disconnected.	Observe cleanliness practices when-ever disconnecting and reconnecting. Clean out foreign material and inspect fitting for damage. If ferrules or seat are damaged, replace the damaged parts.
	Interchange of other manufac-turers' components.	Use only SWAGELOK Tube Fittings. DO NOT INTERCHANGE.
9. Flows are too low in system.	Obstruction in system.	When assembling a system be cautious so that gravel, dirt, sand, or other foreign material does not get in tub-ing or fittings.
	Single ferrule fitting has over-swaged, restricting tube I. D.	
	System sized too small.	Check to determine if system should be constructed of a larger diameter tubing.
10. Fittings cannot be disassem-bled after high temperature operation.	Pipe threads have welded together. Nut threads have welded to threads on tube fitting body.	SILVER GOOP Lubricant should be used on high temperature alloys for operation at high temperatures to 1500° F.

TROUBLE SHOOTING

Trouble	Possible Cause	Recommended Corrective Measures
11. Tubing is deformed after system has been in operation.	Excessive Pressure. Tubing of insufficient tensile strength or wall thickness was used.	Use stronger material or heavier wall tubing.
	Freeze-up of water or condensate in steam tracing.	Prevention through proper installation, operation and maintenance.
12. Polyethylene tubing slips from fitting.	Slippery characteristic of polyethylene material.	Use Nylon or brass SWAGELOK Tube Fittings with polyethylene tubing whenever possible. If polyethylene is required for corrosive or purity reasons, use a polyethylene front ferrule, Nylon or metal back ferrule and a metal nut with a polyethylene fitting body.
13. TFE tubing slips from fitting.	Slippery characteristic of TFE material.	Use TFE front ferrule and stainless back ferrule and nut when connecting TFE tubing.
14. Glass tubing breaks when connecting fitting.	Metal back ferrule used improperly.	Use CAJON Ultra-Torr Fittings. With SWAGELOK Tube Fittings use a Nylon back ferrule. If temperatures above 150° F are to be encountered, use a metal back ferrule but with caution in pull-up.

TROUBLE SHOOTING

Trouble	Possible Cause	Recommended Corrective Measures
15. Seal is not obtained on glass tubing.	Glass tubing is millimeter size and not fractional size.	Use CAJON Ultra-Torr Fittings. Obtain tubing to fractional sizes or use special SWAGELOK Metric Tube Fittings, with Nylon ferrules.
	Glass tubing is undersize. This may happen even if some sections of the tubing are the right size.	Use CAJON Ultra-Torr Fittings. Obtain tubing that is no smaller than .032" (32 thousandths of an inch) in diameter under the designated fractional size. For example: Glass tubing should be at least 0.218" in diameter when used with $1/4$" fittings, etc.
16. Tubing creeps from fitting when using plasticized PVC tubing.	Insert not used with Plasticized PVC Tubing.	Use SWAGELOK Inserts with Plasticized PVC Tubing, or use CAJON Hose Connectors.

CHAPTER VI

TYPES OF FITTINGS

1. *SWAGELOK* TUBE FITTINGS

2. *SWAGELOK* QUICK-CONNECTS

3. VALVES

4. PIPE FITTINGS

5. WELD FITTINGS

6. HIGH PRESSURE TUBE FITTINGS

7. *SWAGELOK* METRIC FITTINGS

CHAPTER VI

TYPES OF *SWAGELOK* TUBE FITTINGS, PART NUMBERS AND
SUMMARY OF *SWAGELOK* FITTING DESIGNATOR CODES

TUBE SIZE DESIGNATORS	
Designator	Tube O.D.
-1	$\frac{1}{16}''$
-2	$\frac{1}{8}''$
-3	$\frac{3}{16}''$
-4	$\frac{1}{4}''$
-5	$\frac{5}{16}''$
-6	$\frac{3}{8}''$
-8	$\frac{1}{2}''$
-10	$\frac{5}{8}''$
-12	$\frac{3}{4}''$
-14	$\frac{7}{8}''$
-16	$1''$
-20	$1\frac{1}{4}''$
-24	$1\frac{1}{2}''$
-32	$2''$

FITTING SERIES DESIGNATORS	
Designator	Design Sizes
0	$\frac{1}{16}''$ to $\frac{3}{8}''$ $1\frac{1}{4}''$ to $2''$
1	over $\frac{3}{8}''$ to $1\frac{1}{8}''$
M	millimeter tube sizes
F	Female SWAGELOK

COMPONENT DESIGNATORS	
Designator	Designates
0	Complete Fitting Assembly
1	Body only (such as Adapter or Port Connector)
2	Nut
3	Front Ferrule
4	Back Ferrule
5	Insert

TYPE OF FITTING DESIGNATORS	
Designator	Type of Fitting
-1-	Male Connector
-2-	Male Elbow
-3	Tee, Union
-3TTF	Tee, Female Branch
-3TFT	Tee, Female Run
-3TTM	Tee, Male Branch
-3TMT	Tee, Male Run
-4	Cross, Union
-5-	45° Male Elbow
-6	Union
-6-	Reducing Union
-7-	Female Connector
-8-	Female Elbow
-9	Elbow, Union
-11-	Bulkhead Male Connector
-61-	Bulkhead Union
-71-	Bulkhead Female Connector
-A-	Adapter (Male if no suffix)
-A1-	Bulkhead Adapter
-C	Cap
-P	Plug
-R-	Reducer

End Connection Designator Suffix	Designates
-AN	37° Male AN Flare
-ANF	37° Female AN Flare
-BT	Bored-through Fitting
-GC	Low Volume Chromatograph Fitting
-F	Female Thread
-K	Knurled Nut
-KN	Knurled Nut, Nylon Ferrules
-KT	Knurled Nut, TFE Ferrules
-M	Metric Tube End
-MPW	Male Pipe Weld
-OR	O-Seal Connection
-ST	Straight Thread with O-Ring (for SAE Ports)
-TSW	Tube Socket Weld
-Numeral	Size of second end connection

TYPICAL *SWAGELOK* PART NUMBERS

MATERIAL	MATERIAL DESIGNATOR		TUBE SIZE DESIGNATOR [Sixteenths/Inch or (MM)]	FITTING SERIES DESIGNATOR	COMPONENT DESIGNATOR		TYPE OF FITTING DESIGNATOR		REDUCED SIZE OR TYPE OF OTHER END [Sixteenths/Inch or (MM)]	COMPLETE PART NUMBER
Brass	B	—	6 (3/8")	0	0 (Complete Assembly)	—	1 (Male Connector)	—	6 (3/8" Male Pipe Thread)	B-600-1-6
Steel	S	—	16 (1")	1	0 (Complete Assembly)	—	2 (Male Elbow)	—	16 (1" Male Pipe Thread)	S-1610-2-16
316 Stainless Steel	SS	—	6 (6 Millimeter)	M	0 (Complete Assembly)	—	6 (Union)	—		SS-6M0-6
Aluminum	A	—	4 (1/4")	0	1 (Body Only)	—	A (Adapter)	—	4 (1/4" Male Pipe Thread)	A-401-A-4
Monel	M	—	6 (3/8")	0	0 (Complete Assembly)	—	9 (Union Elbow)	—		M-600-9
Nylon	NY	—	4 (1/4")	0	0 (Complete Assembly)	—	6 (Reducing Union)	—	2 (Reducing 1/8" Tube)	NY-400-6-2
TFE	T	—	4 (1/4")	0	0 (Complete Assembly)	—	3 (Tee)	—		T-400-3

Mandatory Dash

ORDERING INSTRUCTIONS

The numbering system for SWAGELOK Tube Fittings is designed so that all catalog numbers are prefixed by a MATERIAL DESIGNATOR Code followed by a mandatory dash. Examples: B - (Brass), S - (Steel), SS - (316 Stainless Steel), A - (Aluminum), M - (Monel), NY - (Nylon), T - (TFE).

The SIZE DESIGNATOR following the mandatory dash indicates the tubing O.D. size in sixteenths of an inch (or millimeters).

After the SIZE DESIGNATOR is the FITTING SERIES DESIGNATOR.

After the FITTING SERIES DESIGNATOR is COMPONENT DESIGNATOR.

After the next mandatory dash is the TYPE OF FITTING DESIGNATOR. This number or letter identifies the TYPE OF FITTING (such as male connector, union elbow, reducing union, tee, adapter, etc.).

After the next dash is suffix denoting REDUCED SIZE or TYPE OF OTHER END CONNECTION (if it differs from the first end), also in sixteenths of an inch, (or millimeters).

FITTING TYPES

TO CONNECT TUBING TO A FEMALE PIPE PORT USE:

MALE CONNECTOR

BULKHEAD MALE CONNECTOR

MALE ELBOW

MALE ADAPTER TUBE TO PIPE

MALE RUN TEE

MALE BRANCH TEE

MALE CONNECTOR—TYPE NO. -1-

Sample Part No.

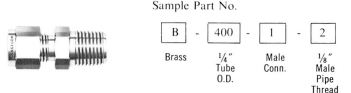

B	-	400	-	1	-	2
Brass		1/4" Tube O.D.		Male Conn.		1/8" Male Pipe Thread

A MALE CONNECTOR is a tube fitting with a SWAGELOK Tube Connection on one end and a male pipe thread on the other end.

BULKHEAD MALE CONNECTOR—TYPE NO. -11-

Sample Part No.

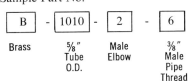

| S | - | 600 | - | 11 | - | 4 |

Steel   ⅜″   Bulkhead   ¼″
       Tube   Male   Male
       O.D.   Conn.   Pipe
                        Thread

A BULKHEAD MALE CONNECTOR is the same as a male connector, but with an additional provision for bulkhead mounting.

MALE ELBOW—TYPE NO. -2-

Sample Part No.

| B | - | 1010 | - | 2 | - | 6 |

Brass   ⅝″   Male   ⅜″
       Tube   Elbow   Male
       O.D.   Pipe
                        Thread

A MALE ELBOW is a tube fitting with a SWAGELOK Tube Connection on one end and a male pipe thread at 90° to the SWAGELOK Tube Connection on the other end.

45° MALE ELBOW—TYPE NO. -5-

Sample Part No.

| B | - | 810 | - | 5 | - | 6 |

Brass   ½″   45°   ⅜″
       Tube   Male   Male
       O.D.   Elbow   Pipe
                        Thread

A MALE ELBOW is a tube fitting with a SWAGELOK Tube Connection on one end and a male pipe thread at 45° to the SWAGELOK Tube Connection on the other end.

MALE ADAPTER TUBE TO PIPE—TYPE NO. -A-

Sample Part No.

| NY | - | 401 | - | A | - | 2 |

Nylon   ¼″   Adapter   ⅛″
       Tube   Male
       Stub   Pipe
       O.D.   Thread

A MALE ADAPTER TUBE TO PIPE is a fitting with a male pipe thread on one end and a machined tube stub on the other end. This adapter converts a female pipe port to a section of tubing on which it is possible to connect a SWAGELOK Tube Connection of proper size.

MALE RUN TEE—TYPE NO. -3TMT

Sample Part No.

S	-	810	-	3TMT
Steel		$\frac{1}{2}$" Tube O.D.		Tee with $\frac{3}{8}$" Male Pipe Thread on run

A TMT TEE is a Tee with a SWAGELOK Tube Connection and a male pipe connection on opposite ends of the run and a SWAGELOK Tube Connection on the branch.*

MALE BRANCH TEE—TYPE NO. -3TTM

Sample Part No.

A	-	400	-	3TTM
Aluminum		$\frac{1}{4}$" Tube O.D.		Tee with $\frac{1}{8}$" Male Pipe Thread on Branch

A TTM TEE is a Tee with SWAGELOK Tube Connections on each end of the run and a male pipe connection on the branch end.*

*Note: Tees are designated by identifying through the run first and then the branch. T is used for Tube; M for Male Pipe.

TO CONNECT TUBING TO A MALE PIPE THREAD USE:

FEMALE CONNECTOR

BULKHEAD FEMALE CONNECTOR

FEMALE ELBOW

FEMALE ADAPTER TUBE TO PIPE

FEMALE RUN TEE

FEMALE BRANCH TEE

FEMALE CONNECTOR—TYPE NO. -7-

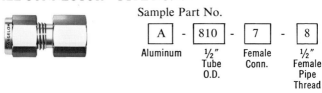

Sample Part No.

A	-	810	-	7	-	8
Aluminum		$\frac{1}{2}$" Tube O.D.		Female Conn.		$\frac{1}{2}$" Female Pipe Thread

A FEMALE CONNECTOR is a tube fitting with a SWAGELOK Tube Connection on one end and a female pipe thread on the other end.

BULKHEAD FEMALE CONNECTOR—TYPE NO. -71-

Sample Part No.

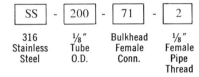

SS	-	200	-	71	-	2
316 Stainless Steel		1/8″ Tube O.D.		Bulkhead Female Conn.		1/8″ Female Pipe Thread

A BULKHEAD FEMALE CONNECTOR is the same as a female connector but with the additional provision for permitting bulkhead mounting.

FEMALE ELBOW—TYPE NO. -8-

Sample Part No.

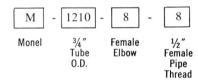

M	-	1210	-	8	-	8
Monel		3/4″ Tube O.D.		Female Elbow		1/2″ Female Pipe Thread

A FEMALE ELBOW is a tube fitting with a SWAGELOK Tube Connection on one end and a female pipe thread at 90° to the SWAGE-LOK Tube Connection on the other end.

FEMALE ADAPTER TUBE TO PIPE—TYPE -A- F

Sample Part No.

B	-	401	-	A	-	4F
Brass		1/4″ O.D. Tube Stub		Adapter		1/4″ Female Pipe Thread

A FEMALE ADAPTER TUBE TO PIPE is a fitting with a female pipe thread on one end and a machined tube stub on the other end. This adapter converts a tube connection of a fitting into a female pipe thread connection.

FEMALE RUN TEE—TYPE NO. -3TFT

Sample Part No.

INC	-	600	-	3TFT
Inconel (600)		³⁄₈″ Tube O.D.		Tee with ½″ Female Thread on run

A TFT TEE is a tee with a SWAGELOK Tube Connection and a female pipe connection on opposite ends of the run and a SWAGELOK Tube Connection on the branch end.

FEMALE BRANCH TEE—TYPE NO. -3TTF

Sample Part No.

Ni	-	1010	-	3TTF
Nickel		⁵⁄₈″ Tube O.D.		Tee with ½″ Female Pipe Thread on branch

A TTF TEE is a tee with SWAGELOK Tube Connections on each end of the run and a Female Pipe Connection on the branch end.

TO CONNECT TWO OR MORE TUBES TOGETHER USE:

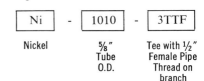
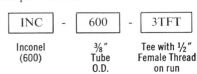

UNION

BULKHEAD UNION

REDUCING UNION

UNION ELBOW

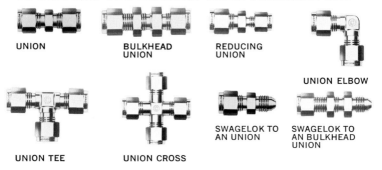

UNION TEE

UNION CROSS

SWAGELOK TO AN UNION

SWAGELOK TO AN BULKHEAD UNION

UNION—TYPE NO -6

Sample Part No.

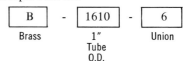

B	-	1610	-	6
Brass		1″ Tube O.D.		Union

A UNION is a tube fitting with SWAGELOK Tube Connections on each end for connecting the same size tubing.

BULKHEAD UNION—TYPE NO. -61

Sample Part No.

| 321 | - | 500 | - | 61 |

| 321 Stainless Steel | 5/16″ Tube O.D. | Bulkhead Union |

A BULKHEAD UNION is the same as a union but with the additional provision for permitting bulkhead mounting.

REDUCING UNION—TYPE NO. -6- (Insert size of tube reduction)

Sample Part No.

| NY | - | 400 | - | 6 | - | 2 |

| Nylon | 1/4″ Tube O.D. | Union | 1/8″ Tube O.D. |

A REDUCING UNION is a tube fitting with two different sizes of SWAGELOK Tube Connections to permit a reduction of tube size.

UNION ELBOW—TYPE NO. -9

Sample Part No.

| SS | - | 200 | - | 9 |

| 316 Stainless Steel | 1/8″ Tube O.D. | Union Elbow |

A UNION ELBOW is a tube fitting with SWAGELOK Tube Connections of the same size at a right angle or 90° to each other.

UNION TEE—TYPE NO. -3

Sample Part No.

| M | - | 600 | - | 3 |

| Monel | 3/8″ Tube O.D. | Union Tee |

A UNION TEE is a tube fitting with SWAGELOK Tube Connections on the run connections and on the branch connection.

UNION CROSS—TYPE NO. -4

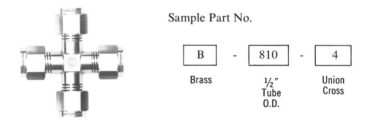

Sample Part No.

B	-	810	-	4
Brass		½" Tube O.D.		Union Cross

A UNION CROSS is a tube fitting with four SWAGELOK Tube Connections each at right angles to adjacent ports.

SWAGELOK TO "AN" (UNION)—TYPE NO. AN

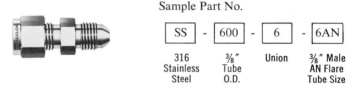

Sample Part No.

SS	-	600	-	6	-	6AN
316 Stainless Steel		⅜" Tube O.D.		Union		⅜" Male AN Flare Tube Size

A SWAGELOK TO "AN" UNION is a tube fitting with a SWAGE-LOK Tube Connection on one end and an AN tube connection (37° flare) on the other end. This fitting is primarily provided to allow adapting and converting existing flare systems to SWAGELOK Tube Connections.

SWAGELOK TO "AN" (BULKHEAD UNION)—TYPE NO. AN

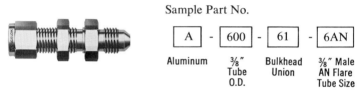

Sample Part No.

A	-	600	-	61	-	6AN
Aluminum		⅜" Tube O.D.		Bulkhead Union		⅜" Male AN Flare Tube Size

A SWAGELOK TO "AN" BULKHEAD UNION is the same as the SWAGELOK To "AN" Union but with provision for bulkhead penetration and mounting.

TO CONNECT TWO OR MORE TUBE FITTINGS TOGETHER USE:

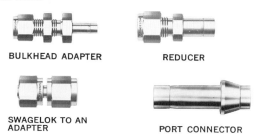

BULKHEAD ADAPTER

REDUCER

SWAGELOK TO AN ADAPTER

PORT CONNECTOR

BULKHEAD ADAPTER—TYPE NO. -A1-

Sample Part No.

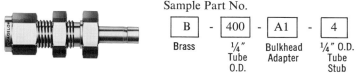

B	-	400	-	A1	-	4
Brass		¼″ Tube O.D.		Bulkhead Adapter		¼″ O.D. Tube Stub

A BULKHEAD ADAPTER is a tube fitting with a SWAGELOK Tube Connection and provision for bulkhead mounting on the SWAGELOK end and a machined tube stub on the other end.

REDUCER—TYPE NO. -R-

Sample Part No.

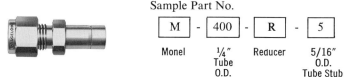

M	-	400	-	R	-	5
Monel		¼″ Tube O.D.		Reducer		5/16″ O.D. Tube Stub

A REDUCER is a tube fitting with a SWAGELOK Tube Connection on one end and a machined tube stub on the other. The SWAGELOK end normally connects tubing of a smaller size than the machined tube stub and permits a reduction in tube size in the fitting.

SWAGELOK TO "AN" (ADAPTER)—TYPE NO. -A- ANF

Sample Part No.

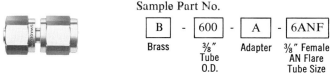

B	-	600	-	A	-	6ANF
Brass		⅜″ Tube O.D.		Adapter		⅜″ Female AN Flare Tube Size

A SWAGELOK TO "AN" ADAPTER is an adapter that will permit connecting a SWAGELOK Tube Fitting to existing Male AN fitting or connection.

PORT CONNECTOR—TYPE NO. -PC

Sample Part No.

B	-	401	-	PC
Brass		¼" O.D. Tube Stub		Port Connector

A PORT CONNECTOR is used to close-connect two components with SWAGELOK ends. The use of a short piece of tubing is eliminated.

TO CAP A TUBE OR PLUG A FITTING USE:
CAP—TYPE NO. -C

Sample Part No.

B	-	200	-	C
Brass		⅛" Tube O.D.		Cap

A SWAGELOK CAP is a SWAGELOK Tube Connection with the other end blanked off for capping the end of a piece of tubing.

PLUG—TYPE NO. -P

Sample Part No.

SS	-	200	-	P
316 Stainless Steel		⅛" Tube O.D.		Plug

A SWAGELOK PLUG is used to plug an unused port of a SWAGE-LOK Tube Fitting.

TO CONNECT TUBING TO PIPE OR STRAIGHT THREAD PORTS USING AN O-RING SEAL USE:

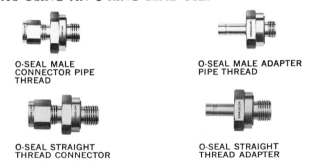

O-SEAL MALE CONNECTOR PIPE THREAD

O-SEAL MALE ADAPTER PIPE THREAD

O-SEAL STRAIGHT THREAD CONNECTOR

O-SEAL STRAIGHT THREAD ADAPTER

O-SEAL MALE CONNECTOR PIPE THREAD—TYPE NO. -OR
(added to part number of male connector of same size)

Sample Part No.

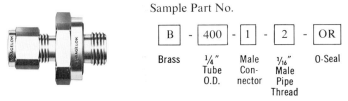

B	-	400	-	1	-	2	-	OR
Brass		1/4″ Tube O.D.		Male Con- nector		1/16″ Male Pipe Thread		O-Seal

An O-SEAL PIPE THREAD CONNECTOR is a tube fitting with a SWAGELOK Tube Connection on one end and a modified male pipe thread on the other end that will fit into a standard female pipe port far enough to allow the O-Ring to seal against a flat surface around the female pipe port.

O-SEAL MALE ADAPTER PIPE THREAD—TYPE NO. -OR
(added to part number of male adapter of same size)

Sample Part No.

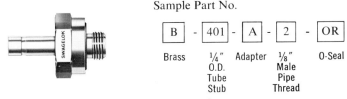

B	-	401	-	A	-	2	-	OR
Brass		1/4″ O.D. Tube Stub		Adapter		1/8″ Male Pipe Thread		O-Seal

An O-SEAL MALE PIPE THREAD ADAPTER is the same as the preceding but with a machined tube stub instead of the SWAGELOK Tube Connection on one end of the fitting.

O-SEAL STRAIGHT THREAD CONNECTOR—TYPE NO. -OR

Sample Part No.

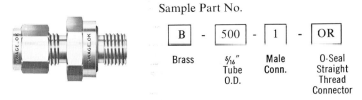

B	-	500	-	1	-	OR
Brass		5/16″ Tube O.D.		Male Conn.		O-Seal Straight Thread Connector

An O-SEAL STRAIGHT THREAD CONNECTOR is a tube fitting with a SWAGELOK Tube Connection on one end and on the other end, a straight thread for screwing into a female straight thread port which allows the O-Ring to seal against a flat surface around the port.

O-SEAL STRAIGHT THREAD ADAPTER—TYPE NO. -A-OR

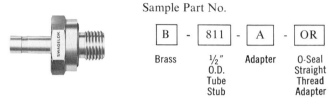

Sample Part No.

B	-	811	-	A	-	OR

Brass   ½″   Adapter   O-Seal
O.D.   Straight
Tube   Thread
Stub   Adapter

An **O-SEAL STRAIGHT THREAD ADAPTER** is the same as the preceding, but with a machined tube stub instead of the **SWAGELOK** Tube Connection on one end of the fitting.

AS SPARE PARTS USE:

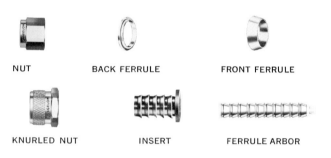

NUT   BACK FERRULE   FRONT FERRULE

KNURLED NUT   INSERT   FERRULE ARBOR

NUT TYPE NO. 2

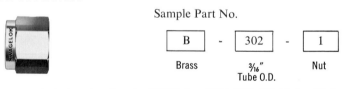

Sample Part No.

B	-	302	-	1

Brass   ³⁄₁₆″   Nut
Tube O.D.

Component designator for the **NUT** for **SWAGELOK** Tube Fittings is "2".

KNURLED NUT TYPE NO. K

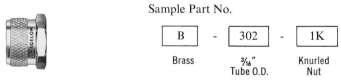

Sample Part No.

B	-	302	-	1K

Brass   ³⁄₁₆″   Knurled
Tube O.D.   Nut

KNURLED NUTS are available in the same sizes as the standard **SWAGELOK** Nut. Add suffix "K" to standard **SWAGELOK** Nut part number.

BACK FERRULE—TYPE NO. 4

Sample Part No.

B	-	604	-	1

Brass   3/8″
Tube O.D.

The component designator for the BACK FERRULE of a SWAGE-LOK Tube Fitting is "4."

FRONT FERRULE—TYPE NO. 3

Sample Part No.

B	-	303	-	1

Brass   3/16″
Tube O.D.

The component designator for the FRONT FERRULE of a SWAGE-LOK Tube Fitting is "3."

INSERT—TYPE NO. 5 · ′

Sample Part No.

B	-	605	-	4

Brass   3/8″ O.D.   1/4″ I.D.
Tubing   Tubing

The component designator for the INSERT is "5."

SWAGELOK Inserts are used in securing soft plastic tubing, such as plasticized PVC or Tygon, with standard SWAGELOK Tube Fittings. To determine the correct SWAGELOK Insert, always check the outside diameter and inside diameter of the plastic tubing. Inserts are not necessary with most plastic tubing. For a complete line of hose connectors see Hose Connector subsection in the Master Catalog Binder.

SWAGELOK Inserts are numbered by size in $1/16$ of an inch in the first digit and a "5" in the component designator tube size designator. The tube I.D. is shown in $1/16$ths after the second mandatory dash.

EXAMPLE—In using Tygon plastic tubing 3/8″ O.D. by 1/4″ I.D. the following parts would be used:

MATERIAL	SWAGELOK FITTING	SWAGELOK INSERT
Brass	B-600-1-4	B-605-4
Aluminum	A-600-1-4	A-605-4
Steel	S-600-1-4	S-605-4
Stainless Steel	SS-600-1-4	SS-605-4
Monel	M-600-1-4	M-605-4
Nylon	NY-600-1-4	NY-605-4

FERRULE-PAK® PACKAGE

The FERRULE-PAK package simplifies ordering, stocking and assembling of both ferrules.

The package offers new convenience at the same prices as individual front-back ferrule sets. It contains 100 ferrule sets, with ten sets rodded on each of ten arbors. Arbors may be dispensed one at a time. The clear plastic cover protects the remaining ferrules in the package, and allows instant check of inventory.

To dispense, simply slide the cover past the top end of the cardboard backing far enough to release one arbor.

To assemble, hold the fitting body vertically and insert the arbor point into the bore of the fitting. Hold a ferrule set firmly with thumb and forefinger and withdraw the arbor. Then tighten the nut finger-tight.

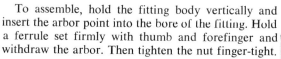

ORDERING INSTRUCTIONS

	CATALOG NUMBER	
TUBE O.D. SIZE	1 FERRULE-PAK QUANTITY (100 SETS)	1 ARBOR QUANTITY (10 SETS)
1/16"	-100 Sets—100	-100 Sets—10
1/8"	-200 Sets—100	-200 Sets—10
1/4"	-400 Sets—100	-400 Sets—10
3/8"	-600 Sets—100	-600 Sets—10
1/2"	-810 Sets—100	-810 Sets—10

To identify materials, use MATERIAL DESIGNATOR Code prefix. (Example: B = Brass, SS = 316 Stainless Steel, etc.)

SWAGELOK KN or KT TUBE FITTINGS MOUNTED ON POLYETHYLENE TUBING

SWAGELOK
BODY

NYLON
FERRULES

KNURLED
NUT

POLYETHYLENE
TUBING

The SWAGELOK KN Fitting provides a leak-tight seal on polyethylene tubing of almost all wall thicknesses without the use of inserts. It consists of a brass **SWAGELOK** Tube Fitting body, nylon ferrules and a knurled nut. To set the ferrules, initial connections are made with a wrench by tightening the nut one-and-one-quarter turns from the finger-tight position. Leakproof reconnections can then be made with finger-tight assembly. Add designator suffix KN for knurled nut with nylon ferrules or KT for knurled nut with TFE ferrules.

FOR SPECIAL CONNECTIONS SUCH AS GAS CHROMATO-GRAPHS, HEAT EXCHANGERS OR THERMOCOUPLES USE:

GC FITTING

HEAT
EXCHANGER TEE

MALE
THERMOCOUPLE
CONNECTOR

GAS CHROMATOGRAPH FITTINGS

Shown is only one of thousands of different Gas Chromatograph Fittings which we make for special applications. Because of the wide variety of end connections, threads, tapers, etc., we only show this low dead volume union as typical of many others. Consult your local SWAGELOK distributor for advice on use of standard configurations to create specials to your order.

HEAT EXCHANGER TEES

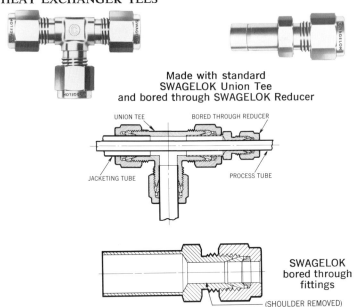

Made with standard
SWAGELOK Union Tee
and bored through SWAGELOK Reducer

UNION TEE   BORED THROUGH REDUCER

JACKETING TUBE   PROCESS TUBE

SWAGELOK
bored through
fittings

(SHOULDER REMOVED)

To order—use part number of SWAGELOK Reducer and add BT (bored through) which will specify O.D. of the PROCESS TUBE.
Example: B-600-R-8BT.
Note: Most users prefer to use our standard reducer and bore it in their own shop. (Remove nuts and ferrules first.)

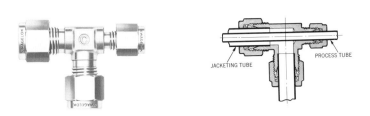

PROCESS TUBE

JACKETING TUBE

Manufactured with any combination of SWAGELOK tube ends.
To order SWAGELOK Heat Exchanger Tees specify in the following order: jacketing tube O.D. x the process tube O.D. x the branch tube O.D.
Example: SS-1210-3-8BT-12.

THERMOCOUPLE CONNECTORS

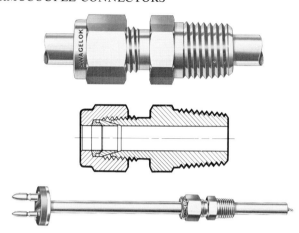

HOW TO MAKE THERMOCOUPLE CONNECTORS

To order, select the desired Male Connector and add suffix BT. For example, SS-400-1-4BT.

Thermocouples or dip tubes are easily handled by SWAGELOK Thermocouple Connectors. They are available in brass, aluminum, steel, stainless steel, Monel and nylon. Other machineable metals and plastics can be furnished when required.

NOTE—The root diameter of the pipe thread end of male connectors makes it impractical to bore through some male connectors. For instance, a -600-1-2 or a -1210-1-8 cannot be bored through without seriously reducing the pipe end strength or destroying the pipe end.

FLEXIBLE METAL HOSE (SERIES DESIGNATOR "H")

Industrial corrugated stainless steel flexible metal hose welded to SWAGELOK Tube Fittings makes up assemblies to be used for installing flexible loops to allow for thermal expansion, misalignment, intermittent flexing and continuous flexure (vibration), in addition to use as static bends. Sample Part No.

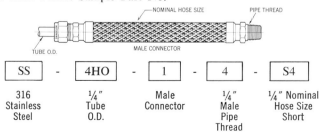

SS	-	4HO	-	1	-	4	-	S4
316 Stainless Steel		¼″ Tube O.D.		Male Connector		¼″ Male Pipe Thread		¼″ Nominal Hose Size Short

SHORT LENGTH (S) INSTALLATION

Once hose has been bent around minimum bend radius, it should not be straightened and re-bent again. This could cause hairline cracks on bellows corrugations. This is particularly important in packaging and handling. Hose should never be tightly coiled and then straightened.

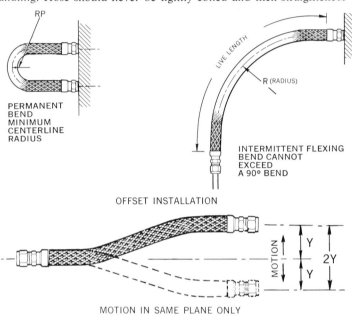

OFFSET INSTALLATION

MOTION IN SAME PLANE ONLY

OFFSET MOTION

OFFSET INSTALLATION OF SHORT LENGTH DIMENSIONS

Nominal Hose Size	Desig- nator Suffix	Y Offset (inches)	R Flexing Bend (inches)	RP Permanent Bend (No Motion) (inches)	"SHORT" Live Hose Length (inches)
1/4 "	S4	1 3/4	5 1/2	7/8	10
3/8 "	S6	2	6	1 1/8	11
1/2 "	S8	2	7	1 1/2	12
3/4 "	S12	2 1/2	8 1/2	2 1/8	14
1 "	S16	3	10	2 3/4	17

LONG LENGTH (L) INSTALLATION

Movement can also be applied when the loop is in a horizontal position, provided that the fixed end of hose is supported as shown.

Note: In hanging loops, both connections and movement should be in same plane.

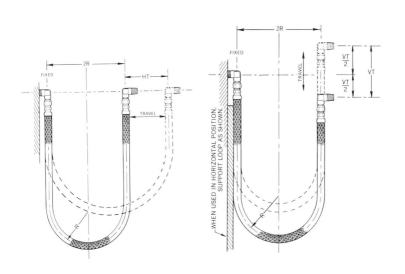

HORIZONTAL TRAVELING LOOP   VERTICAL TRAVELING LOOP

OFFSET INSTALLATION OF LONG LENGTH DIMENSIONS

Nominal Hose Size	Desig- nator Suffix	R (inches)	HT (inches)	VT (inches)	"LONG" Live Hose Length (inches)
1/4 "	L4	5½	6	20	32
3/8 "	L6	6	6	20	34
1/2 "	L8	7	6	20	38
3/4 "	L12	8½	6	20	44
1 "	L16	10	6	20	50

SWAGELOK 1¼″, 1½″ and 2″ TUBE FITTINGS

SWAGELOK Tube Fittings are available in 1¼″, 1½″ and 2″ sizes in both carbon and stainless steel material. The fittings can be used in applications where you are presently using 2″ and smaller nominal size pipe. The fittings replace pipe systems that may be either threaded, welded or flanged. A tubing system in these sizes is more economical with a much improved performance level. To assist installation, Crawford Fitting Company offers an Hydraulic Swaging Tool. It is small, light and portable. This tool is a hand operated device for applying SWAGELOK ferrules to tubing. After this swaging procedure, all that is needed to make a connection is to thread the nut onto the fitting body finger-tight, snug with a wrench ½ turn past finger-tight and the job is complete.

MALE CONNECTOR—TYPE NO. -1-

Sample Part No.

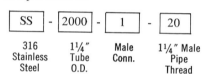

| SS | - | 2000 | - | 1 | - | 20 |

| 316 Stainless Steel | 1¼″ Tube O.D. | Male Conn. | 1¼″ Male Pipe Thread |

A MALE CONNECTOR is a tube fitting with a SWAGELOK Tube Connection on one end and a male pipe thread on the other end.

SWAGELOK CONNECTOR FOR STRAIGHT THREAD BOSS*— TYPE NO. -1-ST

Sample Part No.

| S | - | 2400 | - | 1 | - | 24ST |

| Steel | 1½″ Tube O.D. | Male Conn. | 1½″ Male Straight Thread O-Ring |

*Adapts to MS-33649; AND 10049; AND 10050; JIC and SAE PORTS.

A SWAGELOK Connection for straight thread boss is a tube fitting with a SWAGELOK Tube Connection on one end and on the other end a straight thread for screwing into a female port, to allow the O-ring to seal against a surface inside the port.

UNION—TYPE NO. -6

Sample Part No.

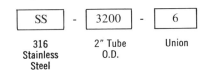

| SS | - | 3200 | - | 6 |

316
Stainless
Steel

2″ Tube
O.D.

Union

A UNION is a tube fitting with SWAGELOK Tube Connections on each end for connecting the same size tubing.

FEMALE CONNECTOR—TYPE NO. -7-

Sample Part No.

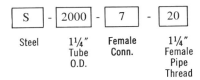

| S | - | 2000 | - | 7 | - | 20 |

Steel

1¼″
Tube
O.D.

Female
Conn.

1¼″
Female
Pipe
Thread

A FEMALE CONNECTOR is a tube fitting with a SWAGELOK Tube Connection on one end and a female pipe thread on the other end.

MALE ELBOW—TYPE NO. -2-

Sample Part No.

| SS | - | 2400 | - | 2 | - | 24 |

316
Stainless
Steel

1½″
Tube
O.D.

Male
Elbow

1½″ Male
Pipe
Thread

A MALE ELBOW is a tube fitting with a SWAGELOK Tube Connection on one end and a male pipe thread at 90° to the SWAGELOK Tube Connection on the other end.

UNION ELBOW—TYPE NO. -9

Sample Part No.

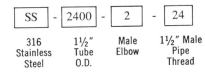

| S | - | 2000 | - | 9 |

Steel

1¼″ Tube
O.D.

Union
Elbow

A UNION ELBOW is a tube fitting with SWAGELOK Tube Connections of the same size at a right angle or 90° to each other.

UNION TEE—TYPE NO. -3

Sample Part No.

SS	-	3200	-	3
316 Stainless Steel		2″ Tube O.D.		Union Tee

A UNION TEE is a tube fitting with SWAGELOK Tube Connections on the run connections and on the branch connection.

MALE ADAPTER TUBE TO PIPE—TYPE NO. -A-

Sample Part No.

S	-	2001	-	A	-	20
Steel		1¼″ O.D. Tube Stub		**Adapter**		1¼″ Male Pipe Size

A MALE ADAPTER TUBE TO PIPE is a fitting with a male pipe thread on one end and a machined tube stub on the other end. This adapter converts a female pipe port to a section of tubing on which it is possible to connect a SWAGELOK Tube Connection of proper size.

FEMALE ADAPTER TUBE TO PIPE—TYPE NO. -A- F

Sample Part No.

SS	-	2401	-	A	-	24F
316 Stainless Steel		1½″ O.D. Tube Stub		**Adapter**		1½″ Female Pipe Size

A FEMALE ADAPTER TUBE TO PIPE is a fitting with a female pipe thread on one end and a machined tube stub on the other end. This adapter converts a tube connection of a fitting into a female pipe thread connection.

ADAPTER FOR STRAIGHT THREAD BOSS*—TYPE -A- ST

Sample Part No.

S	-	3201	-	A	-	32ST
Steel		2″ O.D. Tube Stub		Adapter		2″ Male Straight Thread O-Ring

*Adapts to MS-33649; AND 10049; AND 10050; JIC and SAE Ports.

A SWAGELOK Connection for straight thread boss is a tube fitting with a machined tube stub on one end and on the other end, a straight thread for screwing into a female port, to allow the O-Ring to seal against a surface inside the port.

CAP (FOR CAPPING END OF TUBE)—TYPE NO. -C

Sample Part No.

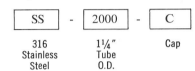

SS	-	2000	-	C
316 Stainless Steel		1¼″ Tube O.D.		Cap

PLUG (FOR PLUGGING UNUSED PORT OF FITTING) TYPE NO. -P

Sample Part No.

SS	-	2000	-	P
316 Stainless Steel		1¼″ Tube O.D.		Plug

NUT—TYPE NO. 2

Sample Part No.

S	-	2402	-	1
Steel		1½″ Tube O.D.		

FRONT FERRULE—TYPE NO. 3

Sample Part No.

SS	-	2403	-	1
316 Stainless Steel		1½″ Tube O.D.		

BACK FERRULE—TYPE NO. 4

Sample Part No.

S	-	3204	-	1
Steel		2″ Tube O.D.		

HYDRAULIC SWAGING UNIT

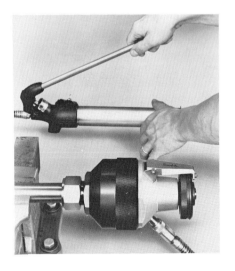

The SWAGELOK Hydraulic Swaging Unit is designed to make a safe and reliable, torque-free, leak-proof seal on large tubing sizes.

For complete information on the SWAGELOK Hydraulic Swaging Unit refer to page 14, Fig. 12.

SWAGELOK QUICK-CONNECTS

STANDARD QUICK-CONNECTS "QC" SERIES

SINGLE END SHUT-OFF

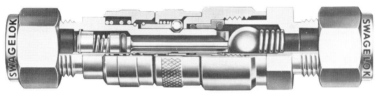

DOUBLE END SHUT-OFF

FULL FLOW QUICK-CONNECTS "QF" SERIES

MINIATURE QUICK-CONNECTS "QM" SERIES

SINGLE END SHUT-OFF

HOW TO ORDER *SWAGELOK* QUICK-CONNECTS

The catalog numbers shown on the following pages contain the designator codes shown below. In all cases the catalog number must be preceded by a material designator; followed by a dash; B- (Brass) and SS- (316 stainless steel).

QUICK-CONNECT SERIES DESIGNATOR	
DESIGNATOR	DENOTES
-QC-	Standard Quick-Connect
-QF-	Full Flow Quick-Connect
-QM-	Miniature Quick-Connect

QUICK-CONNECT SERIES SIZE DESIGNATOR	
DESIGNATOR	DESIGN SIZES
-2	1/8″
-4	1/4″
-6	3/8″
-8	1/2″
-12	3/4″
-16	1″

QUICK-CONNECT MODEL DESIGNATORS	
MODEL DESIGNATOR	DENOTES
-B-	Body
-B1-	Bulkhead Body
-S-	Stem
-S1-	Bulkhead Stem
-D-	Double End Shut-Off Stem
-D1-	Bulkhead Double End Shut-Off Stem
-DC-	Dust Cap (polyethylene only)
-BP-	Body Protector
-SP-	Stem Protector

QUICK-CONNECT END CONNECTION SIZE DESIGNATOR	
DESIGNATOR	SIZE
-1	1/16″
-2	1/8″
-4	1/4″
-6	3/8″
-8	1/2″
-12	3/4″
-16	1″

QUICK-CONNECT END CONNECTION TYPE	
DESIGNATOR	DENOTES TYPE OF END
00	SWAGELOK Tube 1/16″ to 3/8″
10	SWAGELOK Tube 1/2″ to 1″
PM	Pipe, Male NPT
PF	Pipe, Female NPT
AN	37° AN Flare

QUICK-CONNECT SPECIAL DESIGNATOR SUFFIXES	
DESIGNATOR	DENOTES
VT	Viton O-Rings
EP	Ethylene-Propylene O-Rings
SL	Silicone O-Rings
NE	Neoprene O-Rings

Note: All assemblies with O-Rings other than Buna will have inserts made of same material as the body (brass or stainless steel).

TYPICAL *SWAGELOK* QUICK-CONNECT PART NUMBERS

Material	Material Designator		Series Designator	Series Size Designator		Model Designator		End Connection Size	End Connection Type	Complete Part Number
Brass	B	—	QC Standard	4 1/4"	—	D Deso Stem	—	4 1/4"	00 SWAGELOK	B-QC4-D-400
316 Stainless Steel	SS	—	QC Standard	4 1/4"	—	B1 Bulkhead Body	—	4 1/4"	00 SWAGELOK	SS-QC4-B1-400
Brass	B	—	QF Full Flow	12 3/4"	—	S Stem	—	12 3/4"	10 SWAGELOK	B-QF12-S-1210
316 Stainless Steel	SS	—	QF Full Flow	16 1"	—	B Body	—	16 1"	PM Pipe, Male	SS-QF16-B-16PM
Brass	B	—	QM Miniature	2 1/8"	—	S Stem	—	2 1/8"	00 SWAGELOK	B-QM2-S-200
316 Stainless Steel	SS	—	QM Miniature	2 1/8"	—	B Body	—	1 1/16"	PF Pipe, Female	SS-QM2-B-1PF

← Mandatory Dashes →

Page 149

SWAGELOK STANDARD QUICK-CONNECTS, "QC" SERIES WITH SINGLE END AND DOUBLE END SHUT-OFF

SINGLE END SHUT-OFF

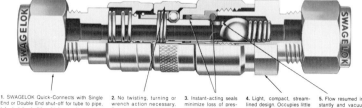

1. SWAGELOK Quick-Connects with Single End or Double End shut-off for tube to pipe, tube to tube, bulkhead tube to tube applications are available in brass and stainless steel in sizes for ¼" to ½" O.D. tubing and pipe.

2. No twisting, turning or wrench action necessary. Easy straight-line finger tip push or pull action for instant connecting or disconnecting.

3. Instant-acting seals minimize loss of pressure when unit is disconnected.

4. Light, compact, streamlined design. Occupies little space. For use with portable equipment and bulkhead or panel applications.

5. Flow resumed instantly and vacuum tight seal assured when connection is made.

DOUBLE END SHUT-OFF

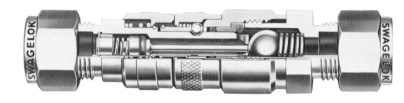

PURPOSE

SWAGELOK "QC" Series Standard Quick-Connects with Single End or Double End shut-off fill the need for compact, easy, push or pull operation to connect and disconnect units for dependable service in hydraulic, pneumatic, fluid transfer, and vacuum systems.

SPECIAL FEATURES

• Reduce time in connection changes with push-to-connect operation.

• Reliable connections in vacuum and pressure systems.

• Use with portable equipment and bulkhead panel systems allows rapid changeover of different pieces of equipment with a single source.

• Automatic shut-off minimizes pressure loss or fluid spillage when disconnecting.

• Compact, in-line valve with no protruding handles.

• In-line shut-off valve requiring no clearance for valve handles.

Page 150

TECHNICAL DATA

Materials

Body, Stem — Brass or 316 stainless steel

Snap Rings and Springs — 302 stainless steel

Balls — 316 stainless steel

O-Ring — Buna in brass; Viton in stainless steel

Insert — Delrin (Metal if other than Buna O-Ring is required)

PRESSURE RATINGS

SWAGELOK Standard Quick-Connects may be safely connected and disconnected at pressures from vacuum to 250 psi. When in the connected position, Standard Quick-Connects may be used at the following recommended maximum safe working pressures:

Standard Quick-Connect Size	Brass (PSI)	316 SS (PSI)
"QC4"	2000	3000
"QC6"	1000	1500
"QC8"	500	750

These ratings may vary according to other system variables.

TEMPERATURE RATINGS

250°F (121°C) with Buna O-Rings and Delrin insert

450°F (232°C) with Viton O-Rings and metal insert

NOTE: When O-Rings other than Buna are ordered, insert is same material as body.

FLOW CAPACITY

"QC4" SERIES				
Maximum Flow	(Single End Cv = .22)		(Deso Cv = .17)	
Pressure Drop To Atmosphere	Air SCFM @ 70°F (21°C)		Water GPM @ 70°F (21°C)	
(△P) PSI	Single End	Deso	Single End	Deso
10	3.04	2.35	.70	.54
25	5.16	3.99	1.10	.85
100	14.92	11.53	2.20	1.70

"QC6" SERIES				
Maximum Flow	(Single End Cv = .79)		(Deso Cv = .56)	
Pressure Drop To Atmosphere	Air SCFM @ 70°F (21°C)		Water GPM @ 70°F (21°C)	
(△P) PSI	Single End	Deso	Single End	Deso
10	10.93	7.75	2.50	1.78
25	18.54	13.14	3.95	2.80
100	53.56	37.97	7.90	5.60

"QC8" SERIES				
Maximum Flow	(Single End Cv = 1.92)		(Deso Cv = 1.27)	
Pressure Drop To Atmosphere (△P) PSI	Air SCFM @ 70°F (21°C)		Water GPM @ 70°F (21°C)	
	Single End	Deso	Single End	Deso
10	26.56	17.57	6.08	4.03
25	45.05	29.80	9.60	6.35
100	130.17	86.10	19.20	12.70

In order to help you avoid stocking unnecessary quantities of stems or bodies, all SWAGELOK Quick-Connects are sold as individual stem or body assemblies. Shown below is a variety of stem and body assemblies with dimensions. Because of the insertion depth of stem into body, only complete 2 piece assembly dimensions are given.

STEM ASSEMBLY

◄— LENGTH —►	TUBE	Single End Shut-Off	Length
	1/4″	-QC4-S-400	2³⁄₁₆
	3/8″	-QC6-S-600	2³⁄₈
	1/2″	-QC8-S-810	2¹⁵⁄₁₆

	TUBE	Double End Shut-Off	Length
	1/4″	-QC4-D-400	2¹⁄₄
	3/8″	-QC6-D-600	2⁷⁄₁₆
	1/2″	-QC8-D-810	2¹⁵⁄₁₆

	TUBE	Bulkhead Single End Shut-Off	Length
	1/4″	-QC4-S1-400	2²³⁄₃₂
	3/8″	-QC6-S1-600	2¹⁵⁄₁₆
	1/2″	-QC8-S1-810	3¹³⁄₃₂

	TUBE	Bulkhead Double End Shut-Off	Length
	1/4″	-QC4-D1-400	2²⁵⁄₃₂
	3/8″	-QC6-D1-600	3
	1/2″	-QC8-D1-810	3¹⁵⁄₃₂

	PIPE	Male Pipe Single End Shut-Off	Length
	1/8″	-QC4-S-2PM	1²⁷⁄₃₂
	1/4″	-QC4-S-4PM	2⁵⁄₃₂
	1/4″	-QC6-S-4PM	2⁵⁄₃₂
	3/8″	-QC6-S-6PM	2¹⁷⁄₃₂
	1/2″	-QC8-S-8PM	2¹³⁄₁₆

NOTE: Dimensions are in inches, for reference only, and are subject to change. Dimensions for SWAGELOK ends are in finger-tight position.

STEM ASSEMBLY

← LENGTH →	PIPE	Female Pipe Single End Shut-Off	Length
	$\frac{1}{8}$ "	-QC4-S-2PF	$1\frac{29}{32}$
	$\frac{1}{4}$ "	-QC4-S-4PF	$2\frac{3}{32}$
	$\frac{1}{4}$ "	-QC6-S-4PF	$2\frac{7}{32}$
	$\frac{3}{8}$ "	-QC6-S-6PF	$2\frac{9}{32}$
	$\frac{1}{2}$ "	-QC8-S-8PF	$2\frac{3}{4}$
	TUBE (AN)	37° AN FLARE Single End Shut-Off	Length
	$\frac{1}{8}$ "	-QC4-S-2AN	$1\frac{59}{64}$
	$\frac{1}{4}$ "	-QC4-S-4AN	$2\frac{1}{64}$
	$\frac{1}{4}$ "	-QC6-S-4AN	$2\frac{9}{64}$
	$\frac{3}{8}$ "	-QC6-S-6AN	$2\frac{5}{32}$
	$\frac{1}{2}$ "	-QC8-S-8AN	$2\frac{23}{32}$

BODY ASSEMBLY

← LENGTH →	TUBE	SWAGELOK Tube Connections	Length
	$\frac{1}{4}$ "	-QC4-B-400	$2\frac{1}{8}$
	$\frac{3}{8}$ "	-QC6-B-600	$2\frac{13}{32}$
	$\frac{1}{2}$ "	-QC8-B-810	$2\frac{29}{32}$
	TUBE	Bulkhead SWAGELOK Tube Connections	Length
	$\frac{1}{4}$ "	-QC4-B1-400	$2\frac{1}{2}$
	$\frac{3}{8}$ "	-QC6-B1-600	$2\frac{13}{16}$
	$\frac{1}{2}$ "	-QC8-B1-810	$2\frac{31}{32}$
	PIPE	Male Pipe	Length
	$\frac{1}{8}$ "	-QC4-B-2PM	$1\frac{25}{32}$
	$\frac{1}{4}$ "	-QC4-B-4PM	$1\frac{31}{32}$
	$\frac{1}{4}$ "	-QC6-B-4PM	$2\frac{3}{16}$
	$\frac{3}{8}$ "	-QC6-B-6PM	$2\frac{3}{16}$
	$\frac{1}{2}$ "	-QC8-B-8PM	$2\frac{25}{32}$
	PIPE	Bulkhead Male Pipe	Length
	$\frac{1}{8}$ "	-QC4-B1-2PM	$2\frac{13}{32}$
	$\frac{1}{4}$ "	-QC6-B1-4PM	$2\frac{13}{16}$
	$\frac{3}{8}$ "	-QC8-B1-6PM	$3\frac{16}{32}$
	PIPE	Female Pipe	Length
	$\frac{1}{8}$ "	-QC4-B-2PF	$1\frac{27}{32}$
	$\frac{1}{4}$ "	-QC4-B-4PF	$2\frac{3}{32}$
	$\frac{1}{4}$ "	-QC6-B-4PF	$2\frac{7}{32}$
	$\frac{3}{8}$ "	-QC6-B-6PF	$2\frac{1}{4}$
	$\frac{1}{2}$ "	-QC8-B-8PF	$2\frac{7}{8}$

NOTE: Dimensions are in inches, for reference only, and are subject to change. Dimensions for SWAGELOK ends are in finger-tight position.

BODY ASSEMBLY

LENGTH	TUBE (AN)	37° AN Flare	Length
	$\frac{1}{8}$"	-QC4-B-2AN	$1\frac{55}{64}$
	$\frac{1}{4}$"	-QC4-B-4AN	$1\frac{61}{64}$
	$\frac{1}{4}$"	-QC6-B-4AN	$2\frac{11}{64}$
	$\frac{3}{8}$"	-QC6-B-6AN	$2\frac{3}{16}$
	$\frac{1}{2}$"	-QC8-B-8AN	$2\frac{11}{16}$

Any "QC4" stem assembly will fit with any "QC4" body assembly, etc.

NOTE: To calculate overall length in connected position, subtract the following from any overall stem and body combination length to allow for insertion depth:

SERIES	DEDUCT
"QC4"	.856" (approx.)
"QC6"	.981" (approx.)
"QC8"	1.263" (approx.)

TABLE OF DIMENSIONS

TUBE TO PIPE

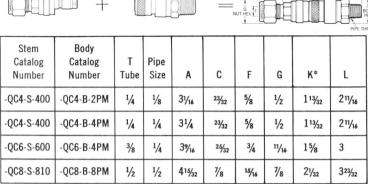

Stem Catalog Number	Body Catalog Number	T Tube	Pipe Size	A	C	F	G	K*	L
-QC4-S-400	-QC4-B-2PM	$\frac{1}{4}$	$\frac{1}{8}$	$3\frac{1}{16}$	$\frac{23}{32}$	$\frac{5}{8}$	$\frac{1}{2}$	$1\frac{13}{32}$	$2\frac{11}{16}$
-QC4-S-400	-QC4-B-4PM	$\frac{1}{4}$	$\frac{1}{4}$	$3\frac{1}{4}$	$\frac{23}{32}$	$\frac{5}{8}$	$\frac{1}{2}$	$1\frac{13}{32}$	$2\frac{11}{16}$
-QC6-S-600	-QC6-B-4PM	$\frac{3}{8}$	$\frac{1}{4}$	$3\frac{9}{16}$	$\frac{25}{32}$	$\frac{3}{4}$	$\frac{11}{16}$	$1\frac{5}{8}$	3
-QC8-S-810	-QC8-B-8PM	$\frac{1}{2}$	$\frac{1}{2}$	$4\frac{15}{32}$	$\frac{7}{8}$	$\frac{15}{16}$	$\frac{7}{8}$	$2\frac{1}{32}$	$3\frac{23}{32}$

For a complete ordering number, add B- for Brass or SS- for 316 Stainless Steel as a prefix to the Catalog Number. *Note: "K" dimension is in disconnected position.

NOTE: Dimensions are in inches, for reference only, and are subject to change. Dimensions for SWAGELOK ends are in finger-tight position.

TUBE TO TUBE

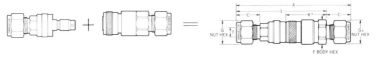

Stem Catalog Number	Body Catalog Number	T Tube	A	C	F	G	Gx	K*	L
-QC4-S-400	-QC4-B-400	$\frac{1}{4}$	$3\frac{13}{32}$	$\frac{23}{32}$	$\frac{5}{8}$	$\frac{1}{2}$	$\frac{9}{16}$	$1\frac{13}{32}$	$2\frac{11}{16}$
-QC6-S-600	-QC6-B-600	$\frac{3}{8}$	$3\frac{25}{32}$	$\frac{25}{32}$	$\frac{3}{4}$	$\frac{11}{16}$	$\frac{11}{16}$	$1\frac{5}{8}$	3
-QC8-S-810	-QC8-B-810	$\frac{1}{2}$	$4\frac{19}{32}$	$\frac{7}{8}$	$\frac{15}{16}$	$\frac{7}{8}$	$\frac{7}{8}$	$2\frac{1}{32}$	$3\frac{23}{32}$

TUBE TO BULKHEAD TUBE

Stem Catalog Number	Body Catalog Number	T Tube	A	C	F	G	Gx	J	K*	L	Panel Hole Drill Size	Max. Panel Thick-ness
-QC4-S-400	-QC4-B1-400	$\frac{1}{4}$	$3\frac{25}{32}$	$\frac{23}{32}$	$\frac{5}{8}$	$\frac{1}{2}$	$\frac{9}{16}$	$1\frac{3}{32}$	$1\frac{13}{32}$	$2\frac{11}{16}$	$\frac{29}{64}$	$\frac{9}{32}$
-QC6-S-600	-QC6-B1-600	$\frac{3}{8}$	$4\frac{3}{16}$	$\frac{25}{32}$	$\frac{3}{4}$	$\frac{11}{16}$	$\frac{11}{16}$	$1\frac{3}{16}$	$1\frac{5}{8}$	3	$\frac{37}{64}$	$\frac{9}{32}$
-QC8-S-810	-QC8-B1-810	$\frac{1}{2}$	$5\frac{1}{16}$	$\frac{7}{8}$	$\frac{15}{16}$	$\frac{7}{8}$	$\frac{7}{8}$	$1\frac{11}{32}$	$2\frac{1}{32}$	$3\frac{23}{32}$	$\frac{49}{64}$	$\frac{9}{32}$

For a complete ordering number, add B- for Brass or SS- for 316 Stainless Steel as a prefix to the Catalog Number. *Note: "K" dimension is in disconnected position.
NOTE: Dimensions are in inches, for reference only, and are subject to change. Dimensions for SWAGELOK ends are in finger-tight position.

SPECIAL ACCESSORIES FOR STANDARD QUICK CONNECTS, "QC" SERIES

To protect "QC" Body Assemblies or Stem Assemblies from damage, dust, or contaminants, protective units are available.

STEM PROTECTOR CAP

Stem Protector Caps are used with standard "QC" Series stems. Caps are available for "QC4", "QC6" and "QC8" sizes in brass or 316 stainless steel, and include a 6″ long bead chain.

BODY PROTECTOR PLUG

Body Protector Plugs are used with standard "QC" Series Body Assemblies. They are available for "QC4", "QC6" and "QC8" sizes in brass or 316 stainless steel and include a 6″ long bead chain.

DUST CAP

Plastic Dust Caps are available for sizes "QC4", "QC6" and "QC8" Body Assemblies.

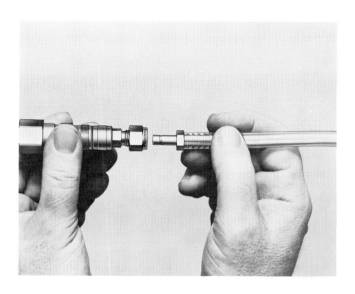

For use with flexible hose, see Hose Connector Subsection of Master Catalog Binder.

SWAGELOK FULL FLOW QUICK-CONNECTS, "QF" SERIES

OPERATION
CONNECT OR DISCONNECT IN SECONDS

To Connect:

1. Slide spring-loaded knurled sleeve back.

2. Insert stem into body until it bottoms.

3. Release sleeve and connection is made when sleeve is in forward position.

To Disconnect:

1. Pull spring loaded knurled sleeve back.
2. Remove stem from body.

PURPOSE

SWAGELOK "QF" Series Full Flow Quick-Connects are designed for maximum flow, and fast, leak-tight connections on rigid or flexible tubing, hose, and piping lines.

APPLICATIONS

SWAGELOK Full Flow Quick-Connects are used in hydraulic and pneumatic systems, gravity flow systems and transfer line connections. They operate in vacuum or pressurized systems at high or low temperatures, and in gas or liquid service.

Other applications include: food processing, chemical research, high pressure systems.

SPECIAL FEATURES

- Full flow without orifice restrictions.
- Permits 360° swivel action.
- SWAGELOK Connections or pipe ends integral with body and/or stem.
- No twisting required for connecting and disconnecting.
- Compact.
- O-Ring can be changed without disassembling body.
- Standard O-Rings used.
- Various end connections available in ¾ " and 1" series.

TECHNICAL DATA

Materials

Body, Stem and Sleeve — Brass or 316 stainless steel
Snap Ring and Springs — 302 stainless steel
Balls — 316 stainless steel
O-Ring — Buna in brass; Viton in stainless steel

Pressure Rating ¾ " and 1" Series

Brass — Vacuum to 3000 psi max.
316 SS — Vacuum to 6000 psi max.

Temperature Ratings

250°F (121°C) with Buna
450°F (232°C) with Viton

FLOW CAPACITY, "QF" SERIES

"QF12" SERIES		
Maximum Flow for Cv = 20		
Pressure Drop to Atmosphere (△P) PSI	Air SCFM @ 70°F (21°C)	Water GPM @ 70°F (21°C)
10	276.70	63.4
25	469.32	100
100	1355.94	200

"QF16" SERIES		
Maximum Flow for Cv = 39		
Pressure Drop to Atmosphere (△P) PSI	Air SCFM @ 70°F (21°C)	Water GPM @ 70°F (21°C)
10	539.57	123.63
25	915.17	195
100	2644.08	390

TABLE OF DIMENSIONS, "QF" SERIES

BODIES

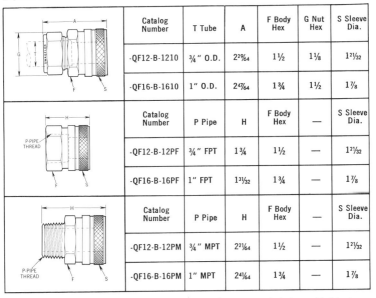

Catalog Number	T Tube	A	F Body Hex	G Nut Hex	S Sleeve Dia.
-QF12-B-1210	¾" O.D.	2²⁹⁄₆₄	1½	1⅛	1²¹⁄₃₂
-QF16-B-1610	1" O.D.	2⁴⁷⁄₆₄	1¾	1½	1⅞

Catalog Number	P Pipe	H	F Body Hex		S Sleeve Dia.
-QF12-B-12PF	¾" FPT	1¾	1½	—	1²¹⁄₃₂
-QF16-B-16PF	1" FPT	1³¹⁄₃₂	1¾	—	1⅞

Catalog Number	P Pipe	H	F Body Hex		S Sleeve Dia.
-QF12-B-12PM	¾" MPT	2²¹⁄₆₄	1½	—	1²¹⁄₃₂
-QF16-B-16PM	1" MPT	2⁴¹⁄₆₄	1¾	—	1⅞

A dimensions are finger-tight   H = overall length   All dimensions are in inches, subject to change

STEMS

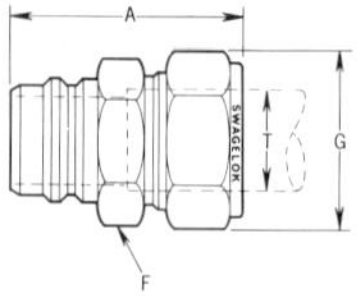

	Catalog Number	T Tube	A	F Stem Hex	G Nut Hex	—
	-QF12-S-1210	¾" O.D.	2⁵⁄₃₂	1¹⁄₁₆	1⅛	—
	-QF16-S-1610	1" O.D.	2²⁷⁄₆₄	1⅜	1½	—
	Catalog Number	P Pipe	H	F Stem Hex	—	—
	-QF12-S-12PF	¾" FPT	1¹⁵⁄₁₆	1¼	—	—
	-QF16-S-16PF	1" FPT	2²¹⁄₆₄	1⅝	—	—
	Catalog Number	P Pipe	H	F Stem Hex	—	—
	-QF12-S-12PM	¾" MPT	2¹⁄₃₂	1¹⁄₁₆	—	—
	-QF16-S-16PM	1" MPT	2²¹⁄₆₄	1⅜		

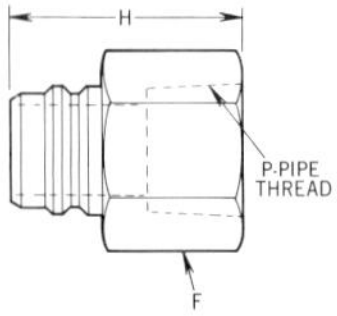

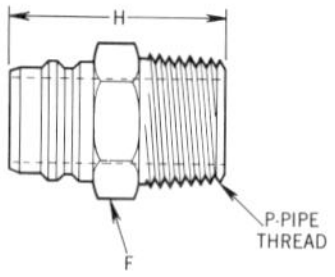

A dimensions are finger-tight   H = overall length   All dimensions are in inches, subject to change

BODY AND STEM ORIFICE

"QF12" series—²³⁄₃₂"
"QF16" series—⅞"

UNIFORM SIZE OF O-RING

"QF12" series—#118
"QF16" series—#215

For a complete ordering number, add B for brass and SS for 316 stainless steel as a prefix to the catalog number.

Maximum assembly length is 3²³⁄₃₂ using body -QF12-B-1210 and stem -QF12-S-1210.

Minimum assembly length is 2⁵¹⁄₆₄ using body -QF12-B-12PF and stem QF12-S-12PF.

Maximum assembly length is 4¹⁷⁄₆₄ using body -QF16-B-1610 and stem -QF16-S-1610.

Minimum assembly length is 3¹³⁄₃₂ using body -QF16-B-16PF and stem -QF16-S-16PF.

NOTE: To calculate overall length in connected position, subtract the following from any overall stem and body combination length to allow for insertion depth:

SERIES	DEDUCT
"QF12"	.891" (approx.)
"QF16"	.918" (approx.)

SWAGELOK MINIATURE QUICK-CONNECTS, "QM" SERIES

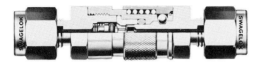

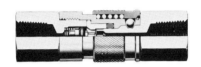

PURPOSE

SWAGELOK "QM" Series Miniature Quick-Connects are designed to fill the need for a lightweight, extremely compact, high performance unit to be used in various fluid handling systems. Where single end shut-off is required, the "QM" series provides a reliable connection with all types of instruments and systems.

SPECIAL FEATURES

- Positive leak-tight seal
- Finger-tip operation
- Lightweight
- Compact
- Allows 360° swivel action
- Low deadspace

APPLICATIONS

Vacuum and pressure systems, electrical coolant lines, chromatographs, control panels, sampling systems, instruments and gauges.

TECHNICAL DATA

Materials

Body and Stem — Brass or 316 stainless steel

Snap Ring and Springs — 302 stainless steel

Balls — 316 stainless steel

Insert — Brass in brass bodies and 316 stainless steel in 316 stainless steel bodies.

O-Ring — Buna in brass; Viton in stainless steel

All Other Parts — Same material as body

Dead Space — .011 in.^{3}

Pressure Ratings

SWAGELOK Miniature Quick-Connects may be connected and

disconnected at pressures from vacuum to 100 psi. Miniature Quick-Connects may be used at higher pressures in the connected position using the following recommended maximum safe working pressure:

Brass—2000 psi
316 SS—4000 psi

Temperature Ratings
250°F (121°C) with Buna O-Rings
450°F (232°C) with Viton O-Rings
Other O-Ring materials available on request

FLOW CAPACITY

"QM" SERIES		
Maximum Flow for Cv = .07		
Pressure Drop to Atmosphere ($\triangle$P) PSI	Air SCFM @ 70°F (21°C)	Water GPM @ 70°F (21°C)
10	.97	.22
25	1.64	.35
100	4.75	.70

TABLE OF DIMENSIONS
FEMALE BODY & STEM

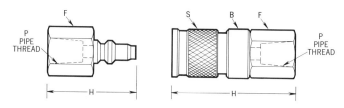

TUBE TO TUBE BODY & STEM

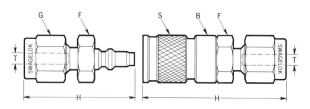

Stem Catalog Number	Body Catalog Number	T Tube	P Pipe	B	F	G	H Stem	H Body	S	Complete Assembly Length
-QM2-S-1PF	-QM2-B-1PF	—	$\frac{1}{16}$	$\frac{1}{2}$	$\frac{7}{16}$	—	$\frac{31}{32}$	$1\frac{9}{32}$	$\frac{33}{64}$	$1\frac{27}{32}$
-QM2-S-200	-QM2-B-200	$\frac{1}{8}$	—	$\frac{1}{2}$	$\frac{7}{16}$	$\frac{7}{16}$	$1\frac{21}{64}$	$1\frac{43}{64}$	$\frac{33}{64}$	$2\frac{1}{2}$

NOTE: Dimensions are in inches, for reference only, and are subject to change. Dimensions for SWAGELOK ends are in finger-tight position.

VALVES

NUPRO Company, WHITEY Company and SNO-TRIK Company offer a wide selection of valves in a variety of materials, body styles, stem types and orifice sizes. NUPRO and WHITEY valves are available with reliable SWAGELOK end connections, as well as a wide range of male and female pipe ends or socket and butt weld. SNO-TRIK valves are offered with high pressure tube fitting ends.

REGULATING & SHUT-OFF VALVES

NUPRO and WHITEY models are available for service conditions from vacuum to 6000 psi and temperatures to 1500°F, with a wide choice of materials, connections, patterns and flow capacities. (In addition, SNO-TRIK Valves are available for high pressure service to 60,000 psi, and temperatures to 650°F.)

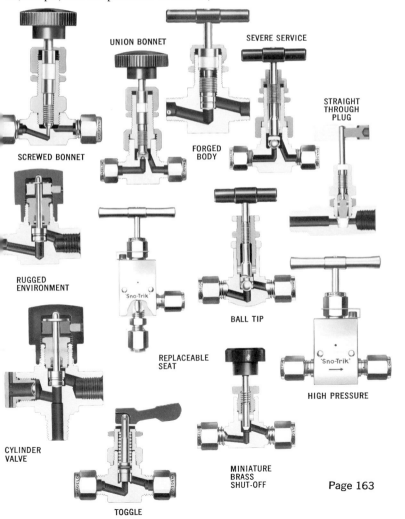

UNION BONNET

SEVERE SERVICE

STRAIGHT
THROUGH
PLUG

SCREWED BONNET

FORGED
BODY

RUGGED
ENVIRONMENT

BALL TIP

REPLACEABLE
SEAT

HIGH PRESSURE

CYLINDER
VALVE

MINIATURE
BRASS
SHUT-OFF

TOGGLE

MANUALLY OPERATED BELLOWS VALVES (PACKLESS)

NUPRO Company offers on-off, regulating and fine metering models for service from vacuum to 2500 psi, and cryogenics to 1500°F.

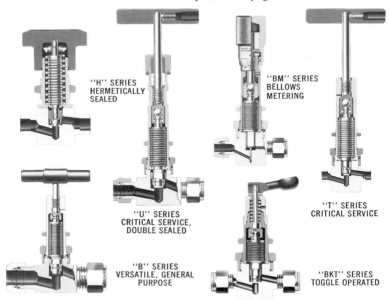

"H" SERIES
HERMETICALLY
SEALED

"BM" SERIES
BELLOWS
METERING

"U" SERIES
CRITICAL SERVICE,
DOUBLE SEALED

"T" SERIES
CRITICAL SERVICE

"B" SERIES
VERSATILE, GENERAL
PURPOSE

"BKT" SERIES
TOGGLE OPERATED

FINE METERING VALVES

NUPRO and WHITEY Valves provide ratings to 5000 psi and 450°F, and are available in a variety of materials, end connections, patterns and flow capacities.

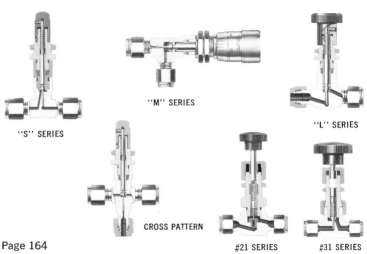

"M" SERIES

"S" SERIES

"L" SERIES

CROSS PATTERN

#21 SERIES

#31 SERIES

CHECK & RELIEF VALVES

NUPRO Company and WHITEY Company, market check and relief valves for pressures to 6000 psi and temperatures from cryogenic to 900°F. For high pressure applications, SNO-TRIK Company offers check valves with pressure ratings to 60,000 psi.

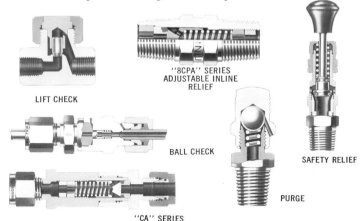

LIFT CHECK

"8CPA" SERIES
ADJUSTABLE INLINE
RELIEF

BALL CHECK

SAFETY RELIEF

PURGE

"CA" SERIES

BALL VALVES

WHITEY Ball Valves are furnished in a variety of designs for quick on-off or switching service at pressures to 3000 psi, in a choice of materials, patterns and end connections.

ON-OFF

ON-OFF
SWING-OUT
DESIGN

3-WAY

4-WAY

5-WAY

PIPE FITTINGS

In order to be acceptable, pipe fittings must be manufactured to meet standards required by the American National Tapered Pipe Thread system or "NPT" threads. However, minor (and sometimes major) leakage has been tolerated as a necessary evil when dealing with piping systems. Why? Because much of the difficulty lies in the process of manufacturing of pipe threads even though these threads may meet the basic NPT requirements.

To further ilustrate this point, Fig. 136 illustrates the basic form of NPT threads.

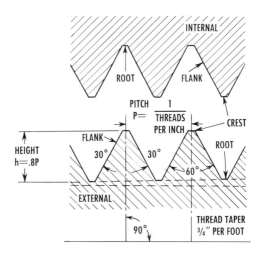

Fig. 136

The basic form of NPT threads, showing roots, flanks and crests is illustrated here. Figs. 137, 138, and 139 illustrate both hand-tight and wrench-tight joints with maximum and minimum thread heights.

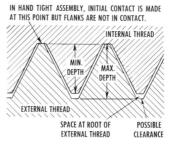

Fig. 137

This illustration shows thread depth variations. Here we find the internal thread cut with a worn tap, resulting in minimum thread depth. The external thread has been cut with sharp tools and the depth is maximum.

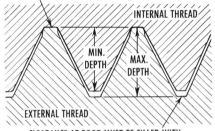

NOTE THE CRUSHED SHAPE OF THE CRESTS,
WHICH ARE FLARED, PREVENTING THE FLANKS
FROM MAKING CONTACT.

INTERNAL THREAD

MIN. DEPTH

MAX. DEPTH

EXTERNAL THREAD

CLEARANCE AT ROOT MUST BE FILLED WITH
PIPE COMPOUND TO PREVENT SPIRAL LEAK

Fig. 138

Above is another example of thread depth variations. The material for both threads is of equal hardness. When wrench is tightened the sharp external thread crests will crush as the thinnest section yields. Three turns of the wrench (tightening) may still not bring the flanks, roots and crests into contact.

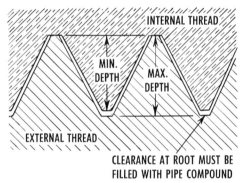

INTERNAL THREAD

MIN. DEPTH

MAX. DEPTH

EXTERNAL THREAD

CLEARANCE AT ROOT MUST BE
FILLED WITH PIPE COMPOUND

Fig. 139

Here is a third example of thread depth variations. Material of the internal thread is softer and less dense than the external thread. When the wrench tightens, the root area on the internal thread will yield and become more compact. The flanks will engage, but there will still remain a void at the root of the external thread.

Since a pipe compound must often be used, it's essential that a compound of good quality be employed. Soap, grease or paint will not remain in place under extensive heat or pressure. Strip Teeze TFE tape is an excellent product to be used instead of pipe compounds.

GAUGING METHODS

A thread that gauges within the limits of plus or minus one turn (on the standard taper pipe plug or ring gauge) is often considered "acceptable." This leaves little consideration for the thread elements *not* checked by these gauges.

Shown below are faulty conditions that can occur when the single gauge method is utilized.

1. Threads not cut to proper length. External threading must have full threads for hand-tight engagement as well as threads that will be engaged when wrench-tightened. When the thread is cut too short as illustrated in Fig. 140 (A), the ring gauge cannot show this fault. When assembled wrench-tight, we are in real trouble. The additional three good threads that are needed for wrench makeup are not available. Fig. 140 (B), shows the result. This same condition can occur with the internal threads tapped too short, leaving no threads at the bottom of the hole for wrench tightening.

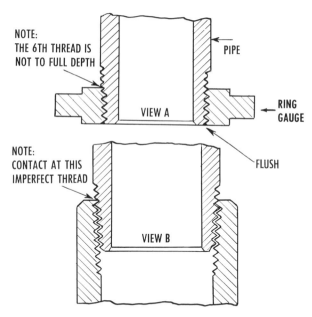

NOTE:
THE 6TH THREAD IS
NOT TO FULL DEPTH

PIPE

VIEW A

RING
GAUGE

NOTE:
CONTACT AT THIS
IMPERFECT THREAD

FLUSH

VIEW B

Fig. 140

Views A and B illustrate the hazard of a short external thread. In view A, there are only five good full threads on the pipe. The ring gauge is flush with the end of the pipe, indicating that the thread is "acceptable". In view B, when assembled wrench-tight in the fitting (which is tapped to maximum size), contact is made on the imperfect thread, and the flanks cannot touch.

2. Side shaved or badly formed threads. It's impossible for the flanks of the mating threads to engage since they have been removed by faulty

cutting equipment. Severely shaved threads will be evidenced by very wide roots and sharp crests. The thread height also will be cut out of tolerance. The conditions that cause side shave are varied. Both external and internal threads can be side shaved and the NPT thread plug or ring gauge will not detect this shortcoming.

3. Drunken threads are most frequently produced by improper thread rolling. However, they can also be made by other means. Here again we find the cause to be faulty pipe threading equipment.

4. Chattered and wavy threads also are caused by poor tools or equipment. Plug or ring gauges do not detect this condition. Chattered threads will not have smooth uniform flanks, roots or crests. As a result, engagement in assembly is only at the high points, and the seal is only possible by pipe compound.

5. Lead errors are not detected by ring or plug gauges (Fig. 141). Here we find an example of minus lead on the internal thread and plus lead on the external thread.

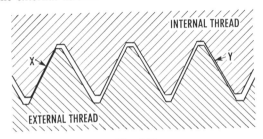

Fig. 141

A condition of lead variation is shown here. Contact at points X and Y keeps the threads from making up properly. The internal thread has slow or minus lead. The external thread has fast or plus lead. The result will be no seal, because the flanks, roots and crests cannot engage.

6. Variations in angle of thread form cannot be checked by ring or plug gauges. Fig. 142 shows the two extremes on 14 pitch pipe threads with tolerance plus or minus 2 degrees.

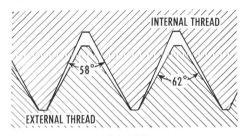

Fig. 142

This drawing shows the extreme condition that is possible with the internal thread at 58 degrees and the external thread at 62 degrees.

7. Flat spot on external or internal thread when pipe is subjected to rough handling. Occasionally the end is dented. If this condition is not noted before the thread is cut, the ring gauge will not detect this shortcoming. A similar condition also occurs on other external and internal pipe threads in castings or forgings not properly filled out.

8. Out-of-round and other eccentric conditions resulting from poor machining practice. If the part is thin it may be bent when clamped, and the threading operation will produce a round thread on the bent piece. When the part is released, it springs back to its original form, and the thread takes on an out-of-round form.

In some cases the mating thread in the assembly will spring the distorted part back, and the problem solves itself in assembly. This condition will not always occur, and leakers result.

9. A slug condition found only in rolled threads occurs when the thread rolling dies are chipped. The slug of metal left in the root of the thread corresponds with the chip in the die.

If the slug is located just beyond the threads gauged, the gauge cannot detect the error. When the fitting is wrench-tightened, the slug will cause interference and prevent proper contact of flanks, crests and roots.

10. Undersize major or oversize minor diameters on threaded parts are responsible for many leaks. Under these conditions, a full thread with proper depth dimension cannot be cut. In both cases the crests are too flat, and thread compound is the only hope of getting the joint to hold pressure.

11. Other conditions such as a torn or chipped thread, a chip clinging to the flank of the thread, and center line of the thread not true with pipe or bore may occur. They cannot be detected by a regular NPT plug or ring gauge. Many of these conditions are not easily detected with any gauge. Careful visual inspection also is important.

The correct use of pipe threads is just as important in assuring leakproof joints as are proper manufacturing and gauging procedures. Since there are many forms of pipe threads, they can become mixed. In some cases, two different threads will mate satisfactorily but aren't reliable for pressure-tight application.

Excessive tightening to make a fitting outlet face the desired direction, or backing off to accomplish the same objective, frequently cause leaks.

How are these problems with pipe fittings to be avoided? The simplest method is to use CAJON Precision Pipe Fittings in your system. CAJON Company assures its customers that all pipe threads on all CAJON Fittings are manufactured to *exceed* specifications as established for NPT thread standards.

To obtain these precision quality pipe threads, all standard CAJON pipe fittings have a rolled male pipe thread. In simple terms, a rolled thread is produced by cold forming or working the material to the desired shape. This process produces beneficial characteristics, such as increased thread strength. Since pipe threads use thread interference to seal, this increase in thread strength becomes an important factor.

High quality surface finish is another benefit obtained from thread rolling. This greatly reduces the tendency for galling common with ordinary threads.

REQUIRED LENGTH OF THREAD ON PIPE
TO MAKE A TIGHT JOINT (APPROXIMATE)

PIPE SIZE (Inches)	DIMENSION B (Inches)	PIPE SIZE (Inches)	DIMENSION B (Inches)
$\frac{1}{8}$	$\frac{1}{4}$	1	$\frac{11}{16}$
$\frac{1}{4}$	$\frac{3}{8}$	$1\frac{1}{4}$	$\frac{11}{16}$
$\frac{3}{8}$	$\frac{3}{8}$	$1\frac{1}{2}$	$\frac{11}{16}$
$\frac{1}{2}$	$\frac{1}{2}$	2	$\frac{3}{4}$
$\frac{3}{4}$	$\frac{9}{16}$		

Dimensions do not allow for variation in tapping or threading.

CAJON INSPECTION REQUIREMENTS

All CAJON Pipe Threads shall be visually inspected and the following conditions shall be cause for rejection: Chattered or wavy thread flanks; Slug conditions caused by chipped thread roll die; Torn thread flanks; Excessive leave-off marks on internal threads (basic wrench makeup dimension position); Torn or chipped thread crests. Due to the extreme care in manufacturing, inspection and product performance. "CAJON Precision Pipe Fittings" are known and well accepted in the field.

When you specify, purchase and install CAJON Precision Pipe Fittings you get the following benefits:

- Machined from barstock or forging materials which meet applicable A.S.T.M. specifications.
- Threads exceed requirements of ASA B2.1 (1968) for tapered pipe threads (N.P.T.).
- Full thread engagement assures reliable makeup of pipe connections.
- Available in many combinations of sizes, multi-step reductions, unusual shapes, and a wide range of materials to reduce the number of fittings needed in a system.
- Attractive finishes meet quality appearance requirements for sophisticated scientific equipment.
- Fittings are properly packaged, with exposed threads protected, to insure delivery undamaged.
- All working pressures in fitting tables are calculated in accordance with Power Piping Code ANSI B31.1 and Refinery Piping Code ANSI B31.3.

Material	Min. Ultimate Tensile Strength	Safety Factor
Brass	40,000 PSI	4:1
Steel	60,000 PSI	3:1
Stainless Steel	75,000 PSI	4:1

TYPES OF *CAJON* PRECISION PIPE FITTINGS
AND PART NUMBERS

The numbering system for CAJON Pipe Fittings is designed so that all part numbers are prefixed by a MATERIAL DESIGNATOR, followed by a dash. Examples: B - (brass), S - (steel), SS - (316 stainless steel). Typical part number: SS-2-HRN-1

For complete list of material and their designators, see the following "MATERIAL DESIGNATOR GUIDE".

■ The SIZE DESIGNATOR following the first dash indicates pipe size in sixteenths of an inch.

■ The letter combination following the SIZE DESIGNATOR identifies the TYPE OF PIPE FITTING.

CN = Close Nipple   E = Elbow

HN = Hex Nipple   SE = Street Elbow

HLN = Hex Long Nipple   RSE = Reducing Street Elbow

HRN = Hex Reducing Nipple   ME = Male Elbow

A = Adapter   T = Tee

RA = Reducing Adapter   ST = Street Tee

RB = Reducing Bushing   BT = Branch Tee

HCG = Hex Coupling   MT = Male Tee

HRCG = Hex Reducing Coupling   CS = Cross

CP = Pipe Cap   UBJ = Union Ball Joint

P = Pipe Plug

■ The number following the TYPE OF FITTING designates the reduced pipe size in sixteenths of an inch (if applicable).

MATERIAL DESIGNATOR GUIDE

MATERIALS - (Metal)	MATERIAL DESIGNATOR
A286 Alloy Steel	A286—
Aluminum Alloys	A—
Brass	B—
CMF22 Chrome Moly Steel	CMF22—
Gold/24 Carat	Gold—
Hastelloy/Alloy B	HB—
Hastelloy/Alloy C-276	HC—
Hastelloy/Alloy X	HX—
Haynes #25	HY25—
Inconel 600	INC—
Inconel X	INCX—
Lead	LEAD—
Magnesium Alloys	MG21A—
Molybdenum	MO—
Monel	M—
Nickel	NI—
Carpenter 20 Cb3 Stainless Steel	C20—
Carpenter 455 Stainless Steel	455—
17-4PH Stainless Steel	174PH—
302 Stainless Steel	302—
303 Stainless Steel	303—
304 Stainless Steel	304—
304L Stainless Steel	304L—
310 Stainless Steel	310—
316 Stainless Steel	SS—
316L Stainless Steel	316L—
321 Stainless Steel	321—
347 Stainless Steel	347—
416 Stainless Steel	416—
Steel (Carbon)	S—
Tantalum	TA—
Titanium	TI—
Zirconium Alloys	ZIRC—

MATERIALS - (Plastic)	MATERIAL DESIGNATOR
Acetal	DEL—
Nylon	NY—
PCTFE Fluorocarbon	KF—
Polyethylene	P—
Polypropylene	PP—
Polyvinyl Chloride	PVC—
TFE Fluorocarbon	T—

CLOSE NIPPLE—TYPE -CN

Sample Part No.

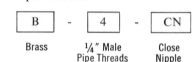

B	-	4	-	CN
Brass		¼″ Male Pipe Threads		Close Nipple

Male NPT both ends. Used to make a straight line close connection between two female threaded components.

HEX NIPPLE—TYPE -HN

Sample Part No.

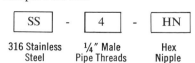

SS	-	4	-	HN
316 Stainless Steel		¼″ Male Pipe Threads		Hex Nipple

Male NPT both ends. Used to make a straight line connection between two female threaded components. Wrench pad for ease of tightening, removal and reuse.

HEX LONG NIPPLE—TYPE -HLN

Sample Part No.

S	-	6	-	HLN	(L)
Steel		⅜″ Male Pipe Threads		Hex Long Nipple	

Male NPT both ends. Use for gauge mounting and extended mounting through installation. Can be drilled and tapped in the field to form manifolds. Produced to specific length requirements to be shown in parentheses following the part number.

HEX REDUCING NIPPLE—TYPE -HRN-

Sample Part No.

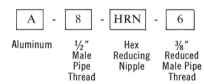

A	-	8	-	HRN	-	6
Aluminum		½″ Male Pipe Thread		Hex Reducing Nipple		⅜″ Reduced Male Pipe Thread

Male NPT to reduced Male NPT. Used to make a reduced straight line connection between two different female threads. Furnishes one step reduction (or more) between thread sizes.

ADAPTER—TYPE -A

Sample Part No.

304	-	16	-	A
304 Stainless Steel		1″ Pipe Threads		Adapter

Female NPT to same size Male NPT. Used as a "sacrifice" fitting to protect threads of valves, gauges, instruments. Also suitable for extending a valve away from equipment to allow for handle swing. Can be modified to include sintered snubber elements.

REDUCING ADAPTER—TYPE -RA-

Sample Part No.

HC	-	8	-	RA	-	2
Hastelloy Alloy "C"		½″ Female Pipe Thread		Reducing Adapter		⅛″ Male Pipe Size

Female NPT to reduced Male NPT. Used like adapter above to increase versatility of various reductions in male to female connections and to eliminate unnecessary connections.

REDUCING BUSHING—TYPE -RB-

Sample Part No.

C20	-	2	-	RB	-	1
Carpenter 20 Stainless Steel		⅛″ Male Pipe Thread		Reducing Bushing		¹⁄₁₆″ Female Pipe Size

Male NPT to reduced Female NPT. Used to increase versatility of various reductions in female to male connections. Eliminates unnecessary connections and allows use of smaller valves and other system components.

HEX COUPLING—TYPE -HCG

Sample Part No.

B	-	12	-	HCG
Brass		¾″ Female Pipe Threads		Hex Coupling

Female NPT both ends. Used to make a straight line connection between two male components.

HEX REDUCING COUPLING—TYPE -HRCG-

Sample Part No.

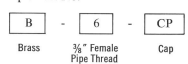

| S | - | 4 | - | HRCG | - | 2 |

Steel   ¼″   Hex   ⅛″
Female   Reducing   Reduced
Pipe Thread   Coupling   Female
Pipe Size

Female NPT to reduced Female NPT. Used for straight line connection between two different size male pipe threads. Furnishes single or multi-step reductions from a basic thread size.

PIPE CAP—TYPE -CP

Sample Part No.

| B | - | 6 | - | CP |

Brass   ⅜″ Female   Cap
Pipe Thread

Female NPT. Used to cap a pipe or male pipe threaded component.

PIPE PLUG—TYPE -P

Sample Part No.

| SS | - | 24 | - | P |

316 Stainless   1½″ Male   Pipe Plug
Steel   Pipe Thread

Male NPT. Used to plug a female threaded component. Substantial wrench pad allows easy make and break.

ELBOW—TYPE -E

Sample Part No.

| S | - | 4 | - | E |

Steel   ¼″ Female   Elbow
Pipe Threads

Female NPT both ends. Used to install male NPT pipe or components at a 90° angle.

STREET ELBOW—TYPE -SE

Sample Part No.

B	-	8	-	SE
Brass		½″ Pipe Threads		Street Elbow

Female to Male NPT. Used to install male to female components at a 90° angle.

REDUCING STREET ELBOW—TYPE -RSE-

Sample Part No.

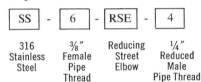

SS	-	6	-	RSE	-	4
316 Stainless Steel		⅜″ Female Pipe Thread		Reducing Street Elbow		¼″ Reduced Male Pipe Thread

Similar to Street Elbow, but used to install male to reduced female NPT components at a 90° angle with single or multi-step reductions.

MALE ELBOW—TYPE -ME

Sample Part No.

S	-	4	-	ME
Steel		¼″ Male Pipe Threads		Male Elbow

Male NPT both ends. Used to install female to female components at a 90° angle where space limitations are critical.

TEE—TYPE -T

Sample Part No.

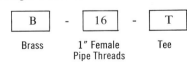

B	-	16	-	T
Brass		1″ Female Pipe Threads		Tee

Female NPT all ports. Used to make a three-way connection of male threaded pipe or components.

STREET TEE—TYPE -ST

Sample Part No.

SS	-	2	-	ST

316
Stainless
Steel

⅛″
Pipe Thread

Street
Tee

Used to make a three-way connection of male-to-female-to-male NPT threaded components.

BRANCH TEE—TYPE -BT

Sample Part No.

S	-	2	-	BT

Steel

⅛″
Pipe Thread

Branch
Tee

Used to make a three-way connection of male-to-male-to-female NPT threaded components.

MALE TEE—TYPE -MT

Sample Part No.

B	-	6	-	MT

Brass

⅜″ Male
Pipe Thread

Male
Tee

Male NPT all ports. Used to make a three-way connection of female threaded components.

CROSS—TYPE -CS

Sample Part No.

SS	-	16	-	CS

316 Stainless
Steel

1″ Female
Pipe Thread

Cross

Used to provide a four-way connection of male NPT pipe or male threaded components.

UNION BALL JOINT—TYPE -UBJ

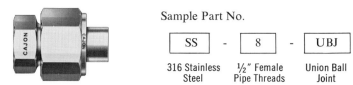

Sample Part No.

SS	-	8	-	UBJ
316 Stainless Steel		½″ Female Pipe Threads		Union Ball Joint

Used to provide a make and break joint between NPT pipe or threaded components. Required between two male components when one or both are fixed. First tighten the UBJ ends to fixed male threaded components, then tighten union nut. Exclusive torque ring reduces make-up problems and enhances life of fitting.

CAJON PIPE FITTINGS FOR ADAPTING NATIONAL PIPE THREADS (NPT) TO INTERNATIONAL PIPE THREADS (ISO)

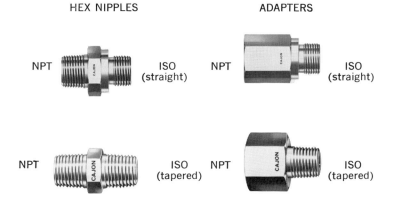

HEX NIPPLES   ADAPTERS

NPT   ISO (straight)   NPT   ISO (straight)

NPT   ISO (tapered)   NPT   ISO (tapered)

Hex Nipples and Adapters from NPT to ISO threads are available from CAJON Company.

Converting imported equipment to standard NPT sizes is no longer a problem. Fittings are available with either male or female NPT to male ISO threads, and are made in brass, steel, or stainless steel.

NPT ends can be obtained in ⅛″, ¼″, ⅜″, and ½″ sizes. The male ISO ends can be straight or tapered and in R⅛, R¼, R⅜, and R½ sizes, for connections to British BSP Whitworth, Din and Keg threads. See pages 216, 222 and 223.

These fittings provide a simple means of transition from a female ISO thread to standard NPT sizes. Also when used in conjunction with a standard SWAGELOK male or female connector, tubing can be connected to female ISO ports. All fittings are clearly marked to indicate proper threads and to avoid damage by cross-threading.

WELD FITTINGS

SWAGELOK and CAJON Weld Fittings are precision machined to meet applicable ASME specifications and ANSI pressure piping codes. Pressure ratings are calculated in accordance with Power Piping Code ANSI B31.1 and Refinery Piping Code ANSI B31.3. Fittings are designed with a 3:1 safety factor for carbon steel and 4:1 safety factor for stainless steel.

BUTT WELDING

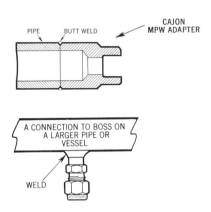

A Butt Weld Fitting, normally welded to a pipe or boss, is butted against the face of the component to which it is to be welded. A circumferential fillet weld is then made at the butt joint.

SOCKET WELDING

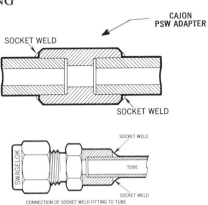

A Socket Weld Fitting has a provision for inserting a tube or pipe into its socket. The fillet weld is then made around the tube or pipe O.D. on the face of the fitting.

SWAGELOK TO WELD FITTINGS

SWAGELOK to weld connections allow easy disassembly of otherwise all welded systems, and provide a transition from welded to non-welded tubing systems.

Installation

When proper methods and precautions are used, SWAGELOK to Weld Fittings will give the usual high quality performance of all other SWAGELOK Tube Fittings.

Completely assembled fittings should not be welded (either pulled up or finger-tight as received) because distortion of the assembly often occurs and lubricants are removed from the nut, making subsequent pull-up or disassembly difficult. The first step in installing a weld fitting is to remove the nuts and ferrules and provide a protecting cap on the tube fitting end as discussed below.

Handling Precautions When Welding

When welding any fitting, regardless of material, care must always be taken so as not to damage the SWAGELOK end or port. If this end is left unprotected, weld spatter during welding can cause damage to threads, machined surfaces, and/or sealing surfaces. This can be eliminated by using a nut or standard fitting plug to cover the thread and seat areas.

The nut or plug needs only to be snugged up by hand to insure protection. This method will allow you to continue using the same nut or plug many times as a protective device while welding.

Material

The choice of fitting material and material being welded is very critical. The same materials will insure the same coefficients of expansion and thus eliminate possibilities of faulty weld, out-of-roundness, dimensional changes, etc., that could be detrimental to a good weld connection.

Welding Procedure

Tack welding at four positions 90° apart will hold the fitting in place while completing the weld. Alignment and concentricity of components are insured by this technique. See Fig. 143 for further alignment information.

Lubricating Precautions After Welding

When welding carbon steel parts, the protective oil coating is often removed by heat. If a SWAGELOK to Weld Fitting is tightened after the oil is removed or has flashed off, there is a chance of galling if no other lubricant such as GOOP is used. Improper pull-up or tightening, which causes a poor connection, could result from poorly lubricated threads.

WELD FITTING MATERIALS

CAJON
S—Steel (C-1018)
SS—Stainless Steel (316)
304L—Stainless Steel (304L)
CMF22—Chrome-Moly Steel

SWAGELOK
A—Aluminum (6061 T6)
B—Brass (Free Cutting)
S—Steel (C-1018)
SS—Stainless Steel (316)

The numbering system for CAJON Weld Fittings is designed so that all part numbers are prefixed by a MATERIAL DESIGNATOR code followed by a dash. Examples: B— (brass), S— (steel), SS— (316 stainless steel), 304L— (304L stainless steel).

The SIZE DESIGNATOR following the dash indicates tube or pipe size in sixteenths of an inch.

The letter combination following the SIZE DESIGNATOR identifies the TYPE OF WELD CONNECTION:

MPW=Male Pipe Weld   PSW=Pipe Socket Weld
MTW=Male Tube Weld   TSW=Tube Socket Weld

The letter or number following the TYPE OF WELD CONNECTION identifies the TYPE OF FITTING:

1—Weld to Male Pipe Connector   7—Weld to Female Pipe Connector
2—Weld to Male Pipe Elbow   8—Weld to Female Pipe Elbow
3—Weld Union Tee   9—Weld Union Elbow
4—Weld Union Cross   A—Adapter
6—Weld Union

The letter or number following the TYPE OF WELD CONNECTING designates the REDUCED SIZE AND TYPE OF END CONNECTION (if applicable).

TYPICAL *CAJON* PART NUMBERS

Material	Desig-nator		Size Designator		Type of Weld Connection		Type of Fitting		Reduced Size on Second End Connection (If Applicable)
Brass	B	–	4	–	TSW	–	1	–	4
316	SS	–	8	–	PSW	–	6	–	
304L	304L	–	6	–	MTW	–	A	–	4TSW
Steel	S	–	12	–	MPW	–	A	–	8TSW

TYPICAL *SWAGELOK* PART NUMBERS

Material	Designator		Size Designator		Type of Fitting		Weld End Size and Type
Steel	S	–	400	–	1	–	4MPW
316	SS	–	400	–	9	–	4TSW
316	SS	–	600	–	2	–	4MPW
Steel	S	–	810	–	6	–	8TSW

TUBE SOCKET WELD MALE CONNECTOR

Sample Part No.

B	-	4	-	TSW	-	1	-	4
Brass		¼″ Tube O.D.		Tube Socket Weld		Male Con- nector		¼″ Male Pipe Thread

A TUBE SOCKET WELD MALE CONNECTOR is used to install welded tube connection to a female threaded pipe port.

TUBE SOCKET WELD MALE ELBOW

Sample Part No.

SS	-	6	-	TSW	-	2	-	6
316 Stainless Steel		⅜″ Tube O.D.		Tube Socket Weld		Male Elbow		⅜″ Male Pipe Thread

A TUBE SOCKET WELD MALE ELBOW is used to install welded tube connection to a female threaded pipe port at a 90° angle.

TUBE SOCKET WELD FEMALE CONNECTOR

Sample Part No.

304L	-	8	-	TSW	-	7	-	8
304L Stainless Steel		½″ Tube O.D.		Tube Socket Weld		Female Con- nector		½″ Female Pipe Thread

A TUBE SOCKET WELD FEMALE CONNECTOR is used to install welded tube connection to a male pipe thread.

TUBE SOCKET WELD FEMALE ELBOW

Sample Part No.

S	-	4	-	TSW	-	8	-	4
Steel		¼″ Tube O.D.		Tube Socket Weld		Female Elbow		¼″ Female Pipe Thread

A TUBE SOCKET WELD FEMALE ELBOW is used to install welded tube connection to a male pipe thread at a 90° angle.

TUBE SOCKET WELD UNION

Sample Part No.

B	-	12	-	TSW	-	6
Brass		3/4″ Tube O.D.		Tube Socket Weld		Union

A TUBE SOCKET WELD UNION is used to install two welded tube connections in a straight line.

TUBE SOCKET WELD UNION ELBOW

Sample Part No.

SS	-	16	-	TSW	-	9
316 Stainless Steel		1″ Tube O.D.		Tube Socket Weld		Union Elbow

A TUBE SOCKET WELD UNION ELBOW is used to install two welded tube connections at a 90° angle.

TUBE SOCKET WELD UNION TEE

Sample Part No.

S	-	2	-	TSW	-	3
Steel		1/8″ Tube O.D.		Tube Socket Weld		Union Tee

A TUBE SOCKET WELD UNION TEE is used for tee-shaped installation of three welded tube connections.

TUBE SOCKET WELD UNION CROSS

Sample Part No.

304L	-	4	-	TSW	-	4
304L Stainless Steel		1/4″ Tube O.D.		Tube Socket Weld		Union Cross

A TUBE SOCKET WELD UNION CROSS is used for cross-shaped installation of four welded tube connections.

PIPE SOCKET WELD UNION

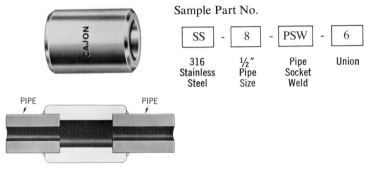

Sample Part No.

| SS | - | 8 | - | PSW | - | 6 |

| 316 Stainless Steel | ½″ Pipe Size | Pipe Socket Weld | Union |

A PIPE SOCKET WELD UNION is used for straight-line installation of two welded pipe connections.

WELD ADAPTERS

Most instrument connections begin at a root valve. This valve is usually a piping specification type, and end connections are either pipe butt weld or pipe socket weld. For years, the transition from pipe size (I.P.S.) to tubing (O.D.) has been a universal problem to installation engineers. The CAJON Company has solved this problem with a complete line of Pipe to Tube Weld Adapters.

CAJON Weld Adapters allow versatility in making weld end connections as follows:

Male Pipe Weld = (MPW)—Also called Pipe Butt Weld
Male Tube Weld = (MTW)—Also called Tube Butt Weld
Pipe Socket Weld = (PSW)
Tube Socket Weld = (TSW)

PIPE TO TUBE WELD ADAPTER

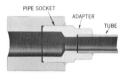

Used to reduce from a pipe socket to a smaller tube size.

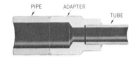

Used to reduce from a pipe butt weld to a smaller tube size.

Sample Part No.

SS	-	6	-	MPW	-	A	-	6TSW
316 Stainless Steel		⅜″ Pipe Weld Size		Male Pipe Weld		Adapter		⅜″ Tube Socket Weld Size

TUBE TO TUBE WELD ADAPTER

Once you are in a complete tubing system the CAJON Company Tube to Tube Weld Adapters can accommodate many of your component requirements.

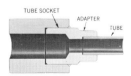

Used to reduce from a tube socket to a smaller tube size.

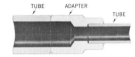

Used to reduce from a tube butt weld to a smaller tube size.

Sample Part No.

304L	-	12	-	MTW	-	A	-	8TSW
304L Stainless Steel		¾″ Tube Fitting O.D.		Male Tube Weld		Adapter		⅜″ Tube Socket Weld Size

CAJON SOCKET WELD FITTINGS CAN BE
PRE-ASSEMBLED BEFORE WELDING

Fig. 143

PRE-ASSEMBLY BEFORE WELDING

All CAJON Socket Weld Fittings incorporate a tapered socket which facilitates system assembly. The taper holds the tubing in place during welding, allowing pre-assembly of several tubing runs before welding. In addition, the tapered socket design improves alignment, and virtually eliminates high stresses in the weld area because the tube end does not bottom out in the fitting socket.

VALVES AVAILABLE WITH BUTT WELD AND
SOCKET WELD ENDS

WHITEY Severe Service Ball Tip Shut-off Valves are available with butt weld and socket weld ends in pressure ratings to 6000 psi. See Regulating and Shut-off Valve Subsection of Master Catalog Binder for complete information.

NUPRO Bellows Valves with butt weld and socket weld ends can be used to handle the most difficult fluid containment problems. Pressures range from vacuum to 2500 psi and temperatures from cryogenic to 1500°F. See Bellows Valve Subsection of Master Catalog Binder for complete information.

SWAGELOK TO WELD FITTINGS
SWAGELOK TO TUBE SOCKET WELD UNION

Sample Part No.

304L	-	810	-	6	-	8TSW
304L Stainless Steel		½″ Tube O.D.		Union		½″ Tube Socket Weld Size

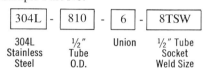

A SWAGELOK to Tube Socket Weld Union is a tube fitting with a SWAGELOK Tube Connection on one end and provision for a socket weld to tubing on the other end.

SWAGELOK TO TUBE SOCKET WELD ELBOW

Sample Part No.

A	-	810	-	9	-	8TSW
Aluminum		½″ Tube O.D.		Elbow Union		½″ Tube Socket Weld Size

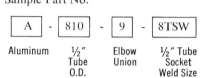

A SWAGELOK to Tube Socket Weld Elbow is a tube fitting with a SWAGELOK Tube Connection on one end and provision for a socket weld to tubing at a 90° angle on the other end.

SWAGELOK TO MALE PIPE WELD CONNECTOR

Sample Part No.

SS	-	200	-	1	-	2MPW
316 Stainless Steel		⅛″ Tube O.D.		Male Connector		⅛″ Male Pipe Weld Size

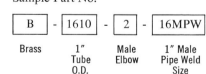

A SWAGELOK to Male Pipe Weld Connector is a tube fitting with a SWAGELOK Tube Connection on one end and provision for a socket connection on the other end.

SWAGELOK TO MALE PIPE WELD ELBOW

Sample Part No.

B	-	1610	-	2	-	16MPW
Brass		1″ Tube O.D.		Male Elbow		1″ Male Pipe Weld Size

A SWAGELOK to Male Pipe Weld Elbow is a tube fitting with a SWAGELOK Tube Connection on one end and a pipe size butt weld connection at a 90° angle on the other end.

HIGH PRESSURE TUBE FITTINGS

Definition of High Pressure:

The term, "High Pressure", cannot be easily defined since it is directly related to specific applications. For example: One individual may consider 1000 psi as "High Pressure", where another individual may consider only applications involving pressures in excess of 100,000 psi as "High Pressure".

In order to measure "High Pressure" for your own application, a PSI Conversion Table is shown below.

PSI CONVERSION TABLE

1 ATM = 14.69 PSI

Individuals working in high pressure often use atmospheres as a unit of pressure measurement. If an exact conversion of ATM's to PSI is required, the figures shown above should be used. However, to facilitate conversion, the following table is based on 1 ATM being equal to approximately 14.7 PSI.

ATM	PSI	ATM	PSI
1	14.7	7,000	102,900
100	1,470	8,500	124,950
500	7,350	10,000	147,000
1,000	14,700	12,000	176,400
3,000	44,100	14,000	205,800
5,000	73,500		

NOTE: At times the term *BAR* may also be used as a unit of pressure measurement. One *BAR* is equal to 14.5 PSI. However, for our purposes, the above table can also be used for approximate conversion of BAR's to PSI.

BACKGROUND

There is one area of high pressure work where very little progress has been made in the last forty or fifty years. This specifically has to do with tube fittings, which are used on heavy wall tubing as applied to high pressure work in the petro-chemical field, pharmaceuticals, and other processes, both production and laboratory.

The fittings used to date, commonly referred to as cone and thread type fittings, were developed by the U.S. Government over forty years ago. Since then, there have been no significant advances made in this area prior to the introduction of SNO-TRIK High Pressure Tube Fittings.

Before dealing with tube fittings specifically, it might be well to first discuss high pressure tubing, materials from which it is manufactured, and its chemical and physical properties.

High pressure tubing comes in many grades. The most commonly supplied is either 304 stainless steel or 316 stainless steel. While 304 stainless steel has good welding capabilities, good mechanical properties and is good for all around corrosion resistance, type 316 has the advantage of being excellent in acid corrosion conditions, good resistance to pitting type corrosion, and high creep strength at high temperatures.

Fig. 144 shows properties of SNO-TRIK 316 stainless steel tubing.

CHEMICAL & PHYSICAL PROPERTIES
SNO-TRIK 316 STAINLESS STEEL TUBE

Chemical Composition %		30,000 psi test			60,000 psi test		
		Ultimate	Yield	Elongation	Ultimate	Yield	Elongation
C .08 Max. Mn 2.00 Max. Si .75 Max. P .03 Max. S .03 Max. Cu .50 Max. Cr 16.0-18.0 Ni 11.0-14.0 Mo 2.0-3.0		70,000 Min.	40,000 to 50,000	35% Min.	110,000 Min.	75,000 to 100,000	20% Min.

Fig. 144

Fig. 145 on tube tolerances, shows commercial tolerances of tube outside diameter, inside diameter, and wall thickness. Other dimensions of the tubing such as ovality and concentricity are also controlled.

COMMERCIAL TUBE TOLERANCES

TUBE O.D.	TOLERANCE		
	O.D.	I.D.	WALL
Up to ³⁄₃₂″ (.09375″)	+.002 −.000	+.000 −.002	±10%
³⁄₃₂″ to ³⁄₁₆″ (.1875″)	+.003 −.000	−.000 +.003	±10%
³⁄₁₆″ to ¹⁄₂″ (.500″)	+.004 −.000	−.000 +.004	±10%
¹⁄₂″ to 1¹⁄₂″ (1.500″)	+.005 −.000	+.000 −.005	±10%

Fig. 145

Stainless steel tubing is generally supplied in three different tempers. *Temper No. 1* is soft annealed, *Temper No. 2* is half-hard, and *Temper No. 3* is full-hard. Micro-inch finish of tubing OD and ID is important and should be controlled. Fig. 146 is a good example of tube ID where micro-inch finish was not controlled. This extreme condition could cause early failure of tubing resulting in damage or loss of process.

Fig. 146

It is well to remember, at this point, that the safety factor applied to the use of high pressure tubing depends entirely on the user. There are no real industry standards published but instead it is up to the individual plant's safety personnel. Fig. 147 gives the dimensions of the tubes most commonly used in high pressure work. These are ¼″, ⅜″, and 9⁄16″.

316 STAINLESS STEEL HEAVY WALL TUBING

Tube O.D. (Inches)	Wall Thickness								SNO-TRIK Fitting Series
	Annealed				Tempered				
	.083	.095	.125	.1875	.083	.095	.125	.1375	
¼	46,400 90,000	50,000 95,000			102,000 110,000	105,000 112,000			440
⅜	25,000 41,000		40,000 81,000				103,000 109,000		640
9⁄16			20,000 36,000	50,000 79,000			58,000 80,000	101,000 105,000	940

Fig. 147

Figures shown in each section are typical yield and ultimate pressures for that tube size. Yield pressures are shown as the top figure. It is recommended the appropriate safety factors be employed for all high pressure applications. Pressure ratings were calculated using typical physical properties for each tube size.

CONE AND THREAD FITTINGS

On the cone and thread type fittings, a left handed thread is cut into the tube O.D. It is by way of these threads that the tube is driven into the mating cone in the body of the fitting. The driving mechanism works through the gland nut and the sleeve. This is clearly shown in Fig. 148.

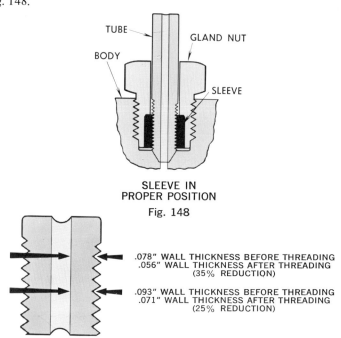

SLEEVE IN
PROPER POSITION
Fig. 148

.078" WALL THICKNESS BEFORE THREADING
.056" WALL THICKNESS AFTER THREADING
(35% REDUCTION)

.093" WALL THICKNESS BEFORE THREADING
.071" WALL THICKNESS AFTER THREADING
(25% REDUCTION)

Fig. 149

Since it is necessary to thread the O.D. of the tube, a loss of from 25 to 35 percent of the wall thickness is suffered, (see Fig. 149). In addition to the loss of wall thickness, the tube now has introduced, about its O.D., a series of stress risers as a result of the threading. Consequently, it is at these points that the tube will fail as a result of vibration. It is easy to see that to prepare the tube for use with the cone and thread type fitting, the tube must first be coned and following this, the tube O.D. must have a thread cut upon it. To do this job properly, a considerable amount of operator experience is required. Various things can go wrong during the threading of the tube O.D. such as thread die closed up too much, causing threads which are under-sized and cut too deeply into the wall of the tube, thread die opened up too much causing an over-sized thread preventing the installation or application of the sleeve. If the thread is not run far enough on the tube O.D., the position of the sleeve will prevent a complete seal in the fitting. If the thread is run too far onto the O.D. of the tube, it can cause additional weakened areas where the tube can fail. It is also necessary that the sleeve be positioned very carefully on the threads of the tube. If not positioned carefully, either an incomplete seal or an over-tightening causing closure of the tube end can result. This is illustrated in Fig. 150. The improper installation of the sleeve can occur either on the original make-up of the fitting or after breaks and remakes of the connection. With the cone and thread type fitting, there is no provision for gauging or checking a fitting to make sure that it has been pulled up properly. The only method to check for leaks is to subject the system to pressure. This could cause loss of time and system process. Since the leak path in the cone and thread type fitting is inherently long, it would take considerable time to detect a leak of very low rate.

INCORRECT INSTALLATION OF THREADED SLEEVE ON TUBE

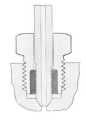
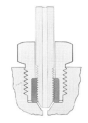

SLEEVE TOO FAR
ON THREAD—TUBE END
COULD CLOSE

SLEEVE NOT ON
THREAD—NO SEAL
ON TUBE CONE END

Fig. 150

SNO-TRIK Fittings overcome these disadvantages as a result of:

1. Not having to thread the O.D. of the tube, thereby maintaining original tube wall thickness and not creating stress risers.

2. Once the SNO-TRIK Fitting has been pulled up, the remakeability is consistent.

3. Preparation of the tube for use of SNO-TRIK Fittings merely requires that the tube end be coned. Because of stringent quality controls and very precise dimensions and close tolerances, it is possible to gauge SNO-TRIK Fittings to make certain that they have been pulled up properly. The leak path or weep port in this fitting is short and direct, providing an immediate indication that the fitting has not been pulled up properly. Because of the dimensioning in the fitting components, it is virtually impossible to over-tighten the fitting to cause tube end closure.

10 GOOD REASONS WHY *SNO-TRIK* TUBE FITTINGS ARE SAFE AND RELIABLE!

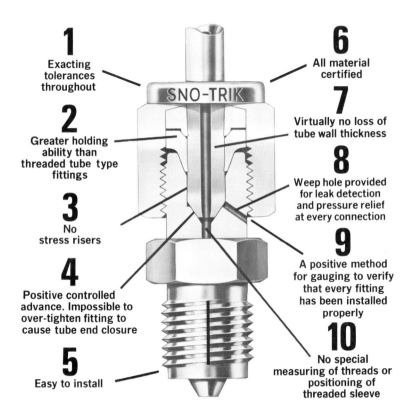

1 Exacting tolerances throughout

2 Greater holding ability than threaded tube type fittings

3 No stress risers

4 Positive controlled advance. Impossible to over-tighten fitting to cause tube end closure

5 Easy to install

6 All material certified

7 Virtually no loss of tube wall thickness

8 Weep hole provided for leak detection and pressure relief at every connection

9 A positive method for gauging to verify that every fitting has been installed properly

10 No special measuring of threads or positioning of threaded sleeve

TECHNICAL DESCRIPTION

SNO-TRIK Fittings prevent weakening of the system caused by reduction of tube wall thickness common to threaded systems ● Unique design and precise manufacturing permit use of an inspection gauge for positive check of proper fitting pull-up ● At 1¼ turns pull-up, the ferrules exert an axial force or pre-load on the tube end which is greater than the rated burst pressure of the tubing ● Back ferrule is manufactured of hardened stainless steel to insure a secure grip on tempered or annealed tubing ● SNO-TRIK Fittings provide a weep hole in the fitting body to avoid tube blow-out caused by improper installation ● SNO-TRIK Fittings grip the tubing without introducing potential failure points inherent with stress risers in threaded tube connections ● The ferrule design provides a high degree of system stability not possible in cone and thread systems, where gaps exist between tube and sleeve threads ● The SNO-TRIK male connector and the wide variety of adapters make SNO-TRIK Fittings readily compatible with any existing system ● SNO-TRIK Fittings prevent excessive deformation of the seal area of tube end and body. If overtightened, a positive controlled advance closes the space between the ferrules rather than overloading and damaging the tube end ● The SNO-TRIK controlled phase sequential gripping action provides holding ability in the first stages of ferrule advance.

SNO-TRIK TUBE FITTINGS PROVIDE INCREASED SAFETY

The tube connection must not be a system's weakest link. For this reason, the cone seal design was developed for heavy wall tube applications.

The rating of tubing depends on its diameter, wall thickness, and the mechanical properties of the material. After wall thickness was increased for higher pressure applications the tube rating then became more dependent on the material strength. Increasing material strength was the next logical step in achieving high pressures.

With the increase in tubing strength, through suitable material processing, the yield strength now approached ultimate strength. This produced a condition of low safety factors for high pressure systems, and now requires an optimum fitting to match the tubing capabilities.

Since the SNO-TRIK Tube Fitting does not reduce the tube wall or introduce stress risers into the tube, there are no added stresses to weaken the system. Through its inherent stability, the SNO-TRIK Fitting provides the safest fitting to match tubing capabiliies.

SNO-TRIK TUBE FITTINGS PROVIDE INCREASED STABILITY

In SNO-TRIK Tube Fittings, the tube is supported in the fitting body by the cone seat, front ferrule, and back ferrule. This provides tube support over a greater length than is possible with a threaded connection, and therefore improves resistance to vibration.

The design of SNO-TRIK Tube Fittings prevents leakage due to tube yield, caused by gaps which always exist in a threaded tube system. When under sustained high pressure, the tubing is stressed, and the strain will cause the tube to yield into these gaps. As the tube yields the seal is lost and the fitting leaks. This potential problem cannot occur in SNO-TRIK Fittings, since the ferrules do not begin their movement onto the tubing until they are in intimate contact with the ramp angles and tube. This ferrule action eliminates gaps, and provides added tubing support. The stress/strain/time relationship is thus prevented, giving a high degree of performance and reliability under pressure cycling, sustained high pressure and vibration.

SEALING ON HEAVY WALL TUBING

In a tube fitting designed for high pressure applications, it is desirable to effect the seal so that the smallest possible area will be exposed to system pressure. This is based on the formula: Force = Pressure × Area. Since the fitting manufacturer has no control over the system pressure, the seal area is minimized in order to control the amount of force exerted against the seal.

This limiting of force is accomplished by coning the tube end, and making the seal on the reduced area of the tube cone. As a safety factor, a weep hole is provided in all SNO-TRIK Tube Fittings. This insures that system pressure would be relieved before exerting greatly increased forces on the larger area of the tube O.D. The inherent safety of the SNO-TRIK Tube Fitting can be demonstrated by the following example:

SNO-TRIK Fitting at 1¼ turns

Example 1.

    A—Area exposed to pressure (.0123 in.²)

    B—Seal Line

    C—¼ ″ OD tube

    P—System pressure 50,000 PSI

    F—Thrust against tube (pounds)

SNO-TRIK Fitting Finger-Tight

Example 2.

    A—Area exposed to pressure (.049 in.²)

    C—¼ ″ OD tube

    P—System pressure 50,000 PSI

    F—Thrust against tube (pounds)

Using the formula: Force = Pressure × Area (F = P × A)

In Example 1	*In Example 2*
F = 50,000 × .0123 in.²	F = 50,000 × .049 in.²
F = 615 lbs.	F = 2,450 lbs.

SNO-TRIK TUBE FITTING INSTALLATION

SNO-TRIK Tube Fittings are installed in 4 easy steps:

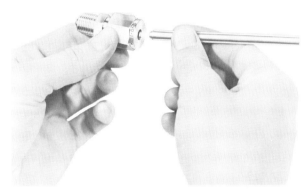

Step 1. Insert properly coned tubing into the SNO-TRIK Tube Fitting. Make sure tube cone rests firmly into the matching internal cone of the fitting. Due to the variation of tubing diameters, snug up the nut until the tubing will not turn (by hand) in the fitting.

Step 2. Then, before tightening the SNO-TRIK nut, scribe a line at the 6:00 o'clock position.

Step 3. While holding the fitting body with a back-up wrench, tighten the nut one-and-one-quarter turns, watching the scribe mark make one complete revolution and continue to the 9:00 o'clock position.

Step 4. Finally, use the SNO-TRIK Inspection Gauge. Insert between the nut and body shoulder to check for proper pull-up of fitting.

RE-TIGHTENING INSTRUCTIONS

Connections can be disconnected and re-tightened many, many times and the same reliable, leakproof seal obtained every time the reconnection is made.

1. Fitting shown in disconnected position.

2. Tubing with pre-set ferrules inserted into the fitting until front ferrule seats in fitting.

3. Tighten nut by hand. Rotate nut about one quarter turn with wrench (or to original one-and-one-quarter tight position), then snug slightly with wrench.

PRE-SETTING INSTRUCTIONS

When SNO-TRIK Tube Fittings are to be installed in cramped quarters or overhead where ladders must be used, it is sometimes found advantageous to use a pre-setting tool on the tubing in an open ground area, thus pre-setting the ferrules. The tubing is then removed from the pre-setting tool and the tubing with nut and pre-set ferrules can now be attached to a fitting merely by following the re-tightening instructions.

SNO-TRIK ORDERING INSTRUCTIONS

SNO-TRIK Tube Connector

Tube O.D.	Size Designator
1/4 "	-440-
3/8 "	-640-
9/16"	-940-

SNO-TRIK High Pressure Male End

Male Thread Size	Size Designator
9/16-18NF	-44M-
3/4-16NF	-64M-
1 1/8-12NF	-94M-

SNO-TRIK Coned Tube Stub

Tube O.D.	Size Designator
1/4 "	-441-
3/8 "	-641-
9/16"	-941-

SNO-TRIK High Pressure Female End

Female Thread Size	Size Designator
9/16-18NF	-44F-
3/4-16NF	-64F-
1 1/8-12NF	-94F-

MATERIALS — Type 316 stainless steel = SS-
   Other materials available on special order.

Material Designator		SNO-TRIK Size & Type Designator		Fitting Type		Second End Size & Type Designator
SS	—	440	—	1	—	44M
SS	—	440	—	1	—	8
SS	—	941	—	A	—	8
SS	—	440	—	R	—	641

SUMMARY OF TYPES OF *SNO-TRIK* FITTINGS

Number used to designate type of fitting in Part Number	TYPE OF FITTING
-1-	Male Connector
-2-	Male Elbow
-3	Tee, Union
-3TTF	Tee, Female Pipe Branch
-3TFT	Tee, Female Pipe Run
-3TTM	Tee, Male Pipe Branch
-3TMT	Tee, Male Pipe Run
-4	Cross, Union
-6	Union
-6-	Reducing Union
-7-	Female Connector
-8-	Female Elbow
-9	Union Elbow
-11-	Bulkhead Male Connector
-61	Bulkhead Union
-71-	Bulkhead Female Connector
-A-	Male Adapter
-A- -F	Female Adapter
-A1-	Bulkhead Adapter
-C	Cap
-P	Plug
-PC	Port Connector
-R-	Reducer
-TSW	Tube Socket Weld
-MPW	Male Pipe Weld
-PSW	Pipe Socket Weld
-MO	Maximum Orifice Fitting

SNO-TRIK HIGH PRESSURE TUBE FITTINGS

SNO-TRIK MALE CONNECTOR—TYPE NO. -1-

Sample Part No.

SS	-	440	-	1	-	44M

316
Stainless
Steel

¼″
Tube
O.D.

Male
Connector

⁹⁄₁₆-18 NF
High Pres-
sure Male
Thread

The MALE CONNECTOR is a tube fitting with a SNO-TRIK Tube Connection on one end and a standard high-pressure male thread and cone on the other end.

SNO-TRIK UNION ELBOW—TYPE NO. -9

Sample Part No.

SS	-	640	-	9

316 Stainless
Steel

⅜″ Tube
O.D.

Union
Elbow

The UNION ELBOW is a tube fitting with SNO-TRIK Tube Connections of the same size at a right angle or 90°.

SNO-TRIK UNION—TYPE NO. -6

Sample Part No.

SS	-	940	-	6

316 Stainless
Steel

⁹⁄₁₆″ Tube
O.D.

Union

The UNION is a tube fitting with SNO-TRIK Tube Connections of the same size on each end of a straight fitting.

SNO-TRIK UNION TEE—TYPE NO. -3

Sample Part No.

SS	-	440	-	3

316 Stainless
Steel

¼″ Tube
O.D.

Union
Tee

The UNION TEE is a tube fitting with SNO-TRIK Tube Connections on the run connections and on the branch connection.

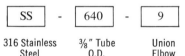

NUT & FERRULE INFORMATION

NUT—TYPE NO. 2

Sample Part No.

| SS | - | 442 | - | 1 |

316 Stainless   ¼" O.D.
Steel   Tube

    The **NUTS** for SNO-TRIK Tube Fittings are numbered by size in ¹⁄₁₆th of an inch (for tube O.D.) in the first digit and a "2" in the component designator.

BACK FERRULE—TYPE NO. 4

Sample Part No.

Standard Back Ferrule material is 17-4PH. To order spare ferrules, use prefix material designator 174PH-. All fittings shown are assembled with 17-4PH Back Ferrules unless otherwise requested. 316 stainless steel Back Ferrules are available on special order. Use prefix SS- when ordering.

| 174PH | - | 444 | - | 1 |

174PH   ¼" O.D.
Stainless Steel   Tube

    The **BACK FERRULE** of a SNO-TRIK Tube Fitting is numbered by size in ¹⁄₁₆ths of an inch in the first digit and a "4" in the component designator.

FRONT FERRULE—TYPE NO. 3

Sample Part No.

| SS | - | 443 | - | 1 |

316 Stainless   ¼" O.D.
Steel   Tube

    The **FRONT FERRULE** of a SNO-TRIK Tube Fitting is numbered by size in ¹⁄₁₆ths of an inch in the first digit and a "3" in the component designator.

SNO-TRIK ADAPTABILITY

SNO-TRIK Tube Fittings enable you to connect most existing ports to SNO-TRIK with a minimum number of connections. All of the configurations shown have been manufactured for customers and many of these are available from stock. All fittings, shown below, are available in sizes for ¼″, ⅜″ and 9/16″ O.D. heavy wall tubing.

BULKHEAD UNION—TYPE NO. -61

Sample Part No.

SS	-	640	-	61
316 Stainless Steel		⅜″ Tube O.D.		Bulkhead Union

The BULKHEAD UNION is the same as a union but with the additional provision for permitting bulkhead penetration and mounting.

SNO-TRIK to SWAGELOK UNION—TYPE NO. -6-

Sample Part No.

SS	-	440	-	6	-	400
316 Stainless Steel		¼″ Tube O.D.		Union		¼″ Tube O.D.

The SNO-TRIK to SWAGELOK UNION allows standard wall tubing to be connected to heavy wall tubing in the same fitting.

SNO-TRIK to CONED TUBE STUB REDUCER—TYPE NO. -R-

Sample Part No.

SS	-	640	-	R	-	941
316 Stainless Steel		⅜″ Tube O.D.		Reducer		• 9/16″ Tube Stub

The REDUCER is a tube fitting with a SNO-TRIK end connection on one end and a machined coned tube stub on the other. The SNO-TRIK end usually connects tubing of a smaller size than the machined tube stub and permits a reduction in tube sizing in the fitting.

SNO-TRIK BULKHEAD to CONED TUBE STUB ADAPTER— TYPE NO. -A1-

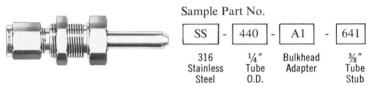

Sample Part No.

SS	-	440	-	A1	-	641

316 Stainless Steel	¼" Tube O.D.	Bulkhead Adapter	⅜" Tube Stub

The BULKHEAD TO CONED TUBE STUB ADAPTER allows bulkhead penetration and mounting along with tube size reduction.

SNO-TRIK to HIGH PRESSURE MALE THREAD REDUCING CONNECTOR—TYPE NO. -1-

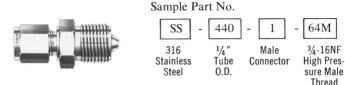

Sample Part No.

SS	-	440	-	1	-	64M

316 Stainless Steel	¼" Tube O.D.	Male Connector	¾-16NF High Pressure Male Thread

The REDUCING MALE CONNECTOR is a tube fitting with a SNO-TRIK Tube Connection on one end and a high pressure male thread of a larger size on the other end.

SNO-TRIK to MALE PIPE THREAD CONNECTOR—TYPE NO. -1-

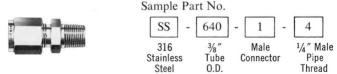

Sample Part No.

SS	-	640	-	1	-	4

316 Stainless Steel	⅜" Tube O.D.	Male Connector	¼" Male Pipe Thread

The SNO-TRIK MALE PIPE THREAD CONNECTOR is a tube fitting with a SNO-TRIK Tube Connection on one end and a male NPT on the other end.

CONED TUBE STUB to MALE PIPE THREAD ADAPTER— TYPE NO. -A-

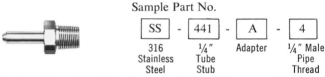

Sample Part No.

SS	-	441	-	A	-	4

316 Stainless Steel	¼" Tube Stub	Adapter	¼" Male Pipe Thread

The SNO-TRIK ADAPTER is a tube fitting with a coned tube stub machined on one end and a male NPT on the other end.

MALE ELBOW—TYPE NO. -2-

Sample Part No.

SS	-	440	-	2	-	4

316
Stainless
Steel

¼″
Tube
O.D.

Male
Elbow

¼″ Male
Pipe
Thread

The MALE ELBOW is a tube fitting with a SNO-TRIK Tube Connection on one end and a male NPT at 90° to the SNO-TRIK end connection on the other end.

MALE BRANCH TEE—TYPE NO. -3TTM

Sample Part No.

SS	-	640	-	3	-	6TTM

316
Stainless
Steel

⅜″
Tube
O.D.

Tee

⅜″ Male
Pipe
Thread

The MALE BRANCH TEE is a tee with SNO-TRIK Tube Connections on each end of run and a male pipe connection on the branch end.

SNO-TRIK to TUBE SOCKET WELD UNION—TYPE NO. -6-

Sample Part No.

SS	-	640	-	6	-	6TSW

316
Stainless
Steel

⅜″
Tube
O.D.

Union

⅜″ Tube
Socket
Weld

The TUBE SOCKET WELD UNION is a tube fitting with a SNO-TRIK Tube Connection on one end and a tube socket weld connection on the other end.

SNO-TRIK to PIPE SOCKET WELD FEMALE CONNECTOR—TYPE NO. -7-

Sample Part No.

SS	-	940	-	7	-	8PSW

316
Stainless
Steel

⁹⁄₁₆″
Tube
O.D.

Female
Connector

½″ Pipe
Socket
Weld

The PIPE SOCKET WELD CONNECTOR has a SNO-TRIK Tube Connection on one end and a pipe socket weld on the other end.

SNO-TRIK to MALE PIPE WELD CONNECTOR—TYPE NO. -1-

Sample Part No.

SS	-	440	-	1	-	4MPW
316 Stainless Steel		¼″ Tube O.D.		Male Connector		¼″ Male Pipe Weld

The MALE PIPE WELD CONNECTOR has a SNO-TRIK Tube Connection on one end and a male pipe weld connection on the other end.

CONED TUBE TUBE to TUBE SOCKET WELD ADAPTER—TYPE NO. -A-

Sample Part No.

SS	-	441	-	A	-	6TSW
316 Stainless Steel		¼″ Tube Stub		Adapter		⅜″ Tube Socket Weld

The TUBE SOCKET WELD ADAPTER has a machined coned tube stub on one end and a tube socket weld connection on the other end.

CONED TUBE STUB to MALE PIPE WELD ADAPTER—TYPE NO. -A-

Sample Part No.

SS	-	441	-	A	-	4MPW
316 Stainless Steel		¼″ Tube Stub		Adapter		¼″ Male Pipe Weld

The MALE PIPE WELD ADAPTER has a machined coned tube stub on one end and a pipe butt weld connection on the other end.

SNO-TRIK to HIGH PRESSURE FEMALE THREAD—TYPE NO. -7-

Sample Part No.

SS	-	440	-	7	-	44F
316 Stainless Steel		¼″ Tube O.D.		Female Connector		$\frac{9}{16}$-18NF High Pressure Female Thread

The FEMALE CONNECTOR has a SNO-TRIK Tube Connection on one end and a standard female high pressure port on the other end. This fitting would be used to connect coned and threadless tubing to coned and threaded tubing.

SNO-TRIK to FEMALE PIPE THREAD CONNECTOR— TYPE NO. -7-

Sample Part No.

SS	-	640	-	7	-	6

316 Stainless Steel   ³⁄₈″ Tube O.D.   Female Connector   ³⁄₈″ Female Pipe Thread

The FEMALE PIPE THREAD CONNECTOR has a SNO-TRIK Connection on one end and a female NPT on the other end.

CONED TUBE STUB to FEMALE PIPE THREAD ADAPTER— TYPE NO. -A-

Sample Part No.

SS	-	941	-	A	-	8F

316 Stainless Steel   ⁹⁄₁₆″ Tube Stub   Adapter   ½″ Female Pipe Thread

The FEMALE PIPE THREAD ADAPTER has a machined coned tube stub on one end and a female NPT on the other end.

PORT CONNECTOR—TYPE NO. -PC

Sample Part No.

SS	-	441	-	PC

NOTE: Reducing Port Connectors also available.

316 Stainless Steel   ¼″ Tube Stub   Port Connector

The PORT CONNECTOR has a machined coned tube stub on one end and machined ferrules and a machined coned tube stub on the other end. This fitting allows two SNO-TRIK end connections to be closely assembled back-to-back.

SNO-TRIK VALVES FOR HIGH PRESSURE

SNO-TRIK shut-off valves provide reliability, safety and long cycle life under the most severe service conditions found in high pressure systems and hazardous or corrosive fluid applications. Also used in medium pressure systems where high safety factors are desirable. For unusually severe applications that require valve replacement, replaceable seat valves are available in angle and cross patterns.

Valve sizes include: ¼ ", ⅜ ", ⁹⁄₁₆" and ⁹⁄₁₆" **MO** (Maximum Orifice). Working pressures as high as 60,000 psi.

TUBE PREPARATION

We recommend that high pressure tubing, used with **SNO-TRIK** Tube Fittings, be coned with a **SNO-TRIK** Coning Tool. For additional information contact your local distributor.

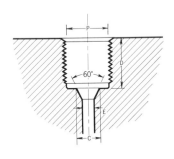

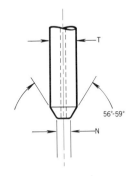

FEMALE PORT FOR MALE CONNECTOR

Typical High Pressure Connections				
Tubing	P	D	E	C
¼	⁹⁄₁₆-18NF	⁷⁄₁₆	³⁄₃₂	³⁄₁₆
⅜	¾-16NF	⅝	⅛	⁹⁄₃₂
⁹⁄₁₆	1⅛-12NF	¾	³⁄₁₆	¹³⁄₃₂

Tube Preparation	
T	N
¼	⅛
⅜	⁷⁄₃₂
⁹⁄₁₆	⁹⁄₃₂

Standard pre-coned tube lengths are available in 2″, 4″, 8″, and 12″ lengths. Tube lengths are precisely coned to the proper angle with a high quality finish for perfect high pressure connections every time.

SNO-TRIK CONING TOOL

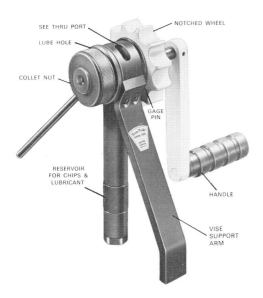

SEE THRU PORT

NOTCHED WHEEL

LUBE HOLE

COLLET NUT

GAGE PIN

RESERVOIR FOR CHIPS & LUBRICANT

HANDLE

VISE SUPPORT ARM

The SNO-TRIK Coning Tool was designed to be used in the preparation of heavy wall tubing. There are two models available. Model #1 will prepare ¼″ O.D. tube only. Model #2 will prepare a tube O.D. range of ¼″, ⅜″, and ⁹⁄₁₆″.

Some of the features designed into this tool are:

• Built-in gauge pin to show where to start and finish the tube cone
• Easily controlled feed of cutting tool • Port for cutting lubricant (CL60) • Ground surfaces for accuracy • Collet grips tube without causing damage to the tube surface during machining • Rust-proof finish • Provision to hold coning tool in bench vise • Easily re-sharpened tool bit • Container to capture chips and used lubricant • Tube cone and tube face machined in one operation.

It is important that the tube cone be prepared correctly since it is one-half of the fitting seal. The SNO-TRIK Coning Tool was designed to do this specific job with accuracy.

CONING TOOL ACCESSORIES

A fitting to adapt the CL60 bottle to the Coning Tool is provided.

CL60 Cutting Lubricant was specially developed for use with the SNO-TRIK Coning Tool when hand machining stainless steel and other tube materials. A bottle of CL60 Lubricant is provided with each Coning Tool.

Collets Furnished with Model #2:

¼"   ⅜"   ⁹⁄₁₆"

Tool Bits Furnished with Model #2:

¼"   ⅜"   ⁹⁄₁₆"

Cone Profiles

One reamer is supplied with each Coning Tool for use in deburring I.D. of the tube.

The Coning Tool and accessories are packaged in a permanent carrying case.

THE METRIC SYSTEM

The Metric System was conceived as a measurement system to the base ten; that is, the units of the system, their multiples and submultiples should be related to each other by simple factors of ten. This is a great convenience because it conforms to our common system for numerical notation, which is also a base ten system. Thus, to convert between units, their multiples and submultiples, it is not necessary to perform a difficult multiplication or division process but simply to shift the decimal point.

THE MODERNIZED METRIC SYSTEM

(National Bureau of Standards; Revised 1970)
The International System of Units (SI) and its
Relationship to U. S. customary units

The International System of Units — officially abbreviated SI — is a modernized version of the metric system. It was established by international agreement to provide a logical and interconnected framework for all measurements in science, industry and commerce. SI is built upon a foundation of base units and their definitions which appear in this section. All other SI units are derived from these base units. Multiples and submultiples are expressed in a decimal system. Use of metric weights and measures was legalized in the United States in 1866, and our customary units of weights and measures are defined in terms of the meter and the kilogram. (The legal units for electricity and illumination in the United States are in SI units).

THE UNITS OF MEASUREMENT

The kilogram shown here approximates the size of the platinum-iridium standard of mass. One pound (avoirdupois) of the same material would be of the size shown.

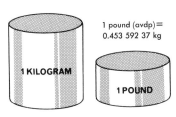

1 pound (avdp)=
0.453 592 37 kg

LENGTH — Meter — m

The meter is defined as 1 650 763.73 wavelengths in vacuum of the orange-red line of the spectrum of Krypton-86.

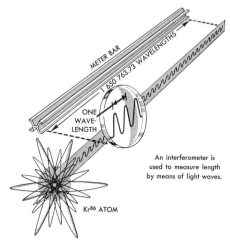

An interferometer is used to measure length by means of light waves.

Kr⁸⁶ ATOM

The SI unit of area is the *square meter* (m²). Land is often measured by the hectare (10,000 square meters, or approximately 2.5 acres).

The SI unit of volume is the cubic meter (m³). Fluid volume is often measured by the liter (0.001 cubic meter).

MASS — Kilogram — kg

The standard for the unit of mass, the kilogram is a cylinder of platinum-iridium alloy kept by the International Bureau of Weights and Measures at Paris. A duplicate in the custody of the National Bureau of Standards serves as the mass standard for the United States.

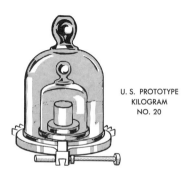

U. S. PROTOTYPE
KILOGRAM
NO. 20

Closely allied to the concept of mass is that of force. The SI unit of force is the *newton* (N). A force of 1 newton, when applied for 1 second, will give to a 1 kilogram mass a speed of 1 meter per second (an acceleration of 1 meter per second).

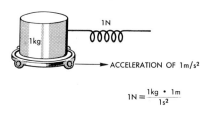

$$1N = \frac{1kg \cdot 1m}{1s^2}$$

One newton equals approximately two tenths of a pound of force.

The weight of an object is the force exerted on it by gravity. Gravity gives a mass downward acceleration of about 9.8 m/s² (meters per second²).

The SI unit for work and energy of any kind is the *joule* (J).

$$1J = 1N \quad 1m$$

The SI unit for power of any kind is the *watt* (W).

$$1W = \frac{1J}{1s}$$

PRESSURE — BAR

The standard SI unit for pressure is the BAR. One BAR = 14.5 PSI for pressures above atmospheric. For pressures below atmospheric (0.95 BAR) such as 1 in. Hg (at 60°F) = 0.034 BAR.

TEMPERATURE—CELSIUS—C

The thermodynamic or Kelvin scale of temperature used in SI has its origin or zero point at absolute zero and has a fixed point at the triple point of water defined as 273.16 Kelvin. The Celsius scale is derived from the Kelvin scale. The triple point is defined as 0.01°C on the Celsius scale which is approximately 32.2°F on the Fahrenheit scale. The relationship of the Kelvin, Celsius and Fahrenheit temperature scales is shown on page 214.

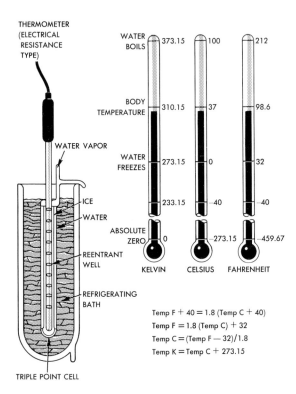

THERMOMETER
(ELECTRICAL
RESISTANCE
TYPE)

WATER BOILS — 373.15 | 100 | 212

BODY TEMPERATURE — 310.15 | 37 | 98.6

WATER VAPOR

WATER FREEZES — 273.15 | 0 | 32

233.15 | -40 | -40

ICE

WATER

ABSOLUTE ZERO — 0 | -273.15 | -459.67

KELVIN   CELSIUS   FAHRENHEIT

REENTRANT WELL

REFRIGERATING BATH

Temp F + 40 = 1.8 (Temp C + 40)
Temp F = 1.8 (Temp C) + 32
Temp C = (Temp F — 32)/1.8
Temp K = Temp C + 273.15

TRIPLE POINT CELL

TRIPLE POINT CELL

The triple point cell, an evacuated glass cylinder filled with pure water, is used to define a known fixed temperature. When the cell is cooled until a mantle of ice forms around the reentrant well, the temperature at the interface of solid, liquid, and vapor is 0.01°C. Thermometers to be calibrated are placed in the reentrant well.

SWAGELOK METRIC TUBE FITTINGS

The recent increase in metric tubing requirements has prompted a SWAGELOK Metric Tube Fitting design. Without doubt, the whole world will go metric. Many forward-looking companies are designing for the future. CRAWFORD FITTING COMPANY is proud to be one of America's leaders in this progress. Adapting to imported equipment will no longer be a problem with new SWAGELOK Metric Tube Fittings.

SWAGELOK Metric Tube Fittings are quite similar in appearance to SWAGELOK Tube Fittings in fractional sizes. The significant difference, however, is in the internal diameter of the tube fitting components. Due to the external similarity between metric and fractional sizes, we have machined a stepped shoulder into the hex body and nut hex to easily identify SWAGELOK Metric Tube Fittings.

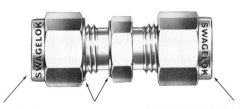

SWAGELOK Metric Tube End   Standard SWAGELOK Tube End (Fractional)

Stepped Shoulder

Elbows and Tees have no step on forging—all forgings are stamped (MM)

In addition to the fittings shown, CRAWFORD FITTING COM-
PANY also makes a wide range of Metric Tube Fittings in sizes from
2MM to 38MM tube sizes. 8MM sizes are not shown. SWAGELOK
500 Series Fractional Tube Fittings will accept 8MM tubing systems.
Please note especially the male and female adapters and unions which
are used to ease the conversion from fractional to metric tubing. Note
also that many fittings are available with ISO threads for connecting to
equipment ports using British BSP Pl, Whitworth, Din and Keg threads,
as well as to equipment utilizing Din, Keg and British BSP Tr tapered
threads. See page 179 for ISO adapters.

ORDERING INSTRUCTIONS

THE SYSTEM — The numbering system for SWAGELOK Metric
Tube Fittings is designed so that all catalog numbers are prefixed by a
MATERIAL DESIGNATOR Code followed by a dash. THE MATE-
RIAL — Examples: B-(Brass), S-(Carbon Steel), SS-(316 Stainless
Steel). For a complete list of Designator Codes, see page 122 of this
manual. THE SIZE — The SIZE DESIGNATOR following the dash
indicates the tubing O.D. in millimeters. The "M" following the size
emphasizes that it is a metric fitting. The last segment of the SIZE DES-
IGNATOR indicates either a complete fitting with nut(s) and ferrules
(O), or an adapter body (1). THE TYPE OF FITTING — After the
next dash is the TYPE OF FITTING DESIGNATOR. This number or
letter identifies the TYPE OF FITTING (such as male connector, union
elbow, union tee, adapter, etc.). THE SECOND END — After the next
dash is the REDUCED SIZE OR TYPE OF END CONNECTION (if
it differs from the first end), in millimeters (M), sixteenths of an inch
$(4 = \frac{1}{4}")$ or ISO threads (R).

TYPICAL METRIC PART NUMBERS

MATERIAL	MATERIAL DESIGNATOR		TUBE SIZE DESIGNATOR		TYPE OF FITTING DESIGNATOR		REDUCED SIZE OR TYPE OF END CONNECTION (MM) OR SIXTEENTH/INCH
Steel	S	—	6 M 0 (6MM, Complete Fitting)	—	6 Union	—	4 ¼" SWAGELOK
316 Stainless Steel	SS	—	10 M 0 (10MM, Complete Fitting)	—	1 Male Connector	—	R ISO — ¼ ¼" Nom. — T Tapered Male Thread
Brass	B	—	12 M 1 (12MM, Body)	—	A Adapter	—	R ISO — ½ ½" Nom. — F Straight Female Thread
Steel	S	—	6 M 0 (6MM, Complete Fitting)	—	1 Male Connector	—	R ISO — ¼ ¼" Nom. — ☐ Straight Male Thread
316 Stainless Steel	SS	—	10 M 0 (10MM, Complete Fitting)	—	6 Union	—	Not Required

MANDATORY DASHES

Your SWAGELOK distributor can supply metric fittings off-the-shelf in many sizes and configurations. The table below is indicative of complete commitment to metrication.

MM Size	Inch Size
2	.0787
3	.1181
4	.1575
6	.2362
8	Use Standard SWAGELOK 500 Series
10	.3937
12	.4724
14	.5512
15	.5905
*16	.6299
18	.7087
20	.7874
22	.8861
25	.9842
28	1.1024
30	1.1811
**38	1.495

*16mm and our Standard 1010 Series, are very close in size; it may be suggested to the customer to try the standard 1010 Series for his application.

**38mm can use our regular 1½″ or 2400 size.

MALE CONNECTOR TO ISO THREAD (STRAIGHT)—
TYPE NO. -1-

Sample Part No.

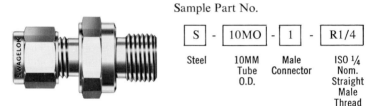

| S | - | 10MO | - | 1 | - | R1/4 |

Steel | 10MM Tube O.D. | Male Connector | ISO ¼ Nom. Straight Male Thread

A MALE CONNECTOR to ISO is a tube fitting used to connect millimeter O.D. tubing to an ISO straight thread female port.

UNION—TYPE NO. -6

Sample Part No.

SS	-	2MO	-	6
316 Stainless Steel		2MM Tube O.D.		Union

A UNION is a tube fitting with SWAGELOK Tube Connections on each end for connecting the same size tubing into both ends.

UNION (METRIC TO FRACTIONAL)—TYPE NO. -6-

Sample Part No.

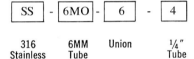

SS	-	6MO	-	6	-	4
316 Stainless Steel		6MM Tube O.D.		Union		¼" Tube O.D.

A UNION is a tube fitting with SWAGELOK Tube Connections on each end for connecting the same size tubing into both ends.

REDUCER (METRIC TO FRACTIONAL)—TYPE NO. -R-

Sample Part No.

B	-	10MO	-	R	-	8
Brass		10MM Tube O.D.		Reducer		½" Tube Stub

A REDUCER is a tube fitting with a SWAGELOK Tube Connection on one end and a machined tube stub on the other. The SWAGELOK end usually connects tubing of a smaller size than the machined tube stub and permits a reduction in tube size in the fitting.

UNION ELBOW—TYPE NO. -9

Sample Part No.

S	-	18MO	-	9
Steel		18MM Tube O.D.		Union Elbow

A UNION ELBOW is a tube fitting with SWAGELOK Tube Connections of the same size at a right angle or 90° to each other.

UNION TEE—TYPE NO. -3

Sample Part No.

SS	-	22MO	-	3
316 Stainless Steel		22MM Tube O.D.		Union Tee

A UNION TEE is a tube fitting tee with SWAGELOK Tube Connections on the run connections and on the branch connection.

MALE ADAPTER—TYPE NO. -A-

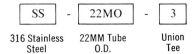

Sample Part No.

B	-	6M1	-	A	-	4
Brass		6MM Tube Stub		Adapter		¼″ Male Pipe Thread

A MALE ADAPTER tube to pipe is a fitting with a male pipe thread on one end and a machined tube stub on the other end. This adapter converts a female pipe port to a section of tubing on which it is possible to connect a SWAGELOK Tube Connection of proper size.

MALE ADAPTER TO ISO THREAD (STRAIGHT)—TYPE NO. -A-

Sample Part No.

B	-	12M1	-	A	-	R1/4
Brass		12MM Tube Stub		Adapter		ISO ¼″ Nom. Straight Male Thread

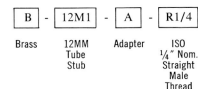

A MALE ADAPTER to ISO is a fitting with a straight male thread on one end and a machined tube stub on the other end. This adapter is used to adapt a millimeter port of a SWAGELOK Tube Fitting to ISO straight thread female port.

FEMALE ADAPTER—TYPE NO. -A-

Sample Part No.

| S | - | 10M1 | - | A | - | 4F |

Steel   10MM   Adapter   ¼″ Female
        Tube Stub   Pipe Thread

A FEMALE ADAPTER tube to pipe is a fitting with a female pipe thread on one end and a machined tube stub on the other end. This adapter converts a tube connection of a fitting into a female pipe thread connection.

FEMALE ADAPTER TO ISO (STRAIGHT)—TYPE NO. -A-

Sample Part No.

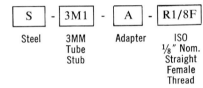

| S | - | 3M1 | - | A | - | R1/8F |

Steel   3MM   Adapter   ISO
        Tube   ⅛″ Nom.
        Stub   Straight
                              Female
                              Thread

A FEMALE ADAPTER to ISO is a fitting with a straight female thread on one end and a machined tube stub on the other end. This adapter is used to adapt a millimeter port of a SWAGELOK Tube Fitting to a male ISO straight thread.

CAP (FOR CAPPING END OF TUBE)—TYPE NO. -C

Sample Part No.

| SS | - | 12MO | - | C |

316 Stainless   12MM Tube   Cap
   Steel   O.D.

A SWAGELOK CAP is a SWAGELOK Tube Connection with the other end blanked off for capping the end of a piece of tubing.

PLUG (FOR PLUGGING UNUSED PORT OF FITTING)—TYPE NO. -P

Sample Part No.

| B | - | 6MO | - | P |

Brass   6MM Tube   Plug
        O.D.

A SWAGELOK PLUG is used to plug an unused port of a SWAGE-LOK Tube Fitting

NUT—TYPE NO. 2

Sample Part No.

| S | - | 10M2 | - | 1 |

Steel   10MM Tube
O.D.

The NUTS for SWAGELOK Tube Fittings are numbered by size in ¹⁄₁₆th of an inch in the first digit and a "2" in the component designator.

BACK FERRULE—TYPE NO. 4

Sample Part No.

| SS | - | 6M4 | - | 1 |

316 Stainless   6MM Tube
Steel   O.D.

The BACK FERRULE of a SWAGELOK Tube Fitting is numbered by size in ¹⁄₁₆ths of an inch in the first digit and a "4" in the component.

FRONT FERRULE—TYPE NO. 3

Sample Part No.

| SS | - | 6M3 | - | 1 |

316 Stainless   6MM Tube
Steel   O.D.

The FRONT FERRULE of a SWAGELOK Tube Fitting is numbered by size in ¹⁄₁₆ths of an inch in the first digit and a "3" in the component.

SWAGELOK INTERNATIONAL PIPE THREADS
Parallel and Tapered Reference Chart

I. INTERNATIONAL STANDARDS ORGANIZATION (ISO) PARALLEL OR STRAIGHT PIPE THREADS

SWAGELOK Designation:
R1/8, R1/4, etc.
EXAMPLE: B-400-1-R1/4—SWAGE-LOK male connector with ¼ʺ ISO parallel pipe threads conforming to ISO Standard R-228.

The parallel or straight thread system is used where a pressure tight seal is NOT made on the thread. The following thread forms also conform to ISO Standard R-228 and are merely different descriptions for identical threads.

1. Whitworth Parallel
2. DIN-259
3. R1/8; etc. (German)
4. BSP Pl (British Parallel as per B.S.-21:1957

II. INTERNATIONAL STANDARDS ORGANIZATION (ISO) TAPERED PIPE THREADS

SWAGELOK Designation:
R1/8T, R1/4T, R3/8T, etc.

EXAMPLE: B-400-1-R1/4—SWAGE-LOK male connector with ¼" ISO tapered pipe threads conforming to ISO Standard R-7.

The tapered pipe thread system is used where a pressure tight seal IS made on the thread. The following thread forms also conform to ISO Standard R-7 and are merely different descriptions for identical threads.

1. DIN-2999
2. R1/8 keg; etc. (German)
3. BSP Tr (British tapered as per B.S.-21:1957)

APPENDIX

CRAWFORD FITTING COMPANY is not responsible for the accuracy of information that appear in the charts and tables in this Appendix. All information is for reference only.

APPENDIX
SECTION I

DETERMINING INSIDE DIAMETER OF TUBING

The I.D. of tubing is set by flow requirements, permissible pressure drop and maximum allowable velocity. To aid in selecting the proper I.D. of tubing for liquid flow, Charts I-1 through I-7 are provided on the following pages. Charts I-8 through I-14 are provided for sizing tubing for gas flow.

These charts give pressure drop for 100 feet of tubing for both water and air flow. By using the formula provided, it is also possible to obtain the pressure drop of fluids other than water and gas.

To allow for pressure drops in bends and fittings, the equivalent lengths in table I-1 can be used when obtaining equivalent length of tubing for pressure drop calculations. To obtain equivalent length of tubing, total all straight lengths and then add lengths for each bend, elbow or tee, from the table I-1.

TABLE I-1					
Equivalent Feet of Straight Tube					
Tubing O.D.	90° Elbow	90° Bend	180° Bend	45° Bend	Tee Branch
¼ "	1 Ft.	½ Ft.	1 Ft.	½ Ft.	1 Ft.
⅜ "	1½ Ft.	½ Ft.	1 Ft.	½ Ft.	1½ Ft.
½ "	2 Ft.	½ Ft.	1 Ft.	½ Ft.	2 Ft.
⅝ "	2½ Ft.	1 Ft.	2 Ft.	½ Ft.	2½ Ft.
¾ "	3 Ft.	1 Ft.	2 Ft.	½ Ft.	3 Ft.
1 "	4½ Ft.	1 Ft.	2 Ft.	½ Ft.	4½ Ft.

CALCULATIONS FOR LIQUID FLOW

EXAMPLE: 1 . Water is to flow through 50 feet of tubing at 4 Gallons per minute (GPM). Water velocity is not to exceed 5 feet per second. The maximum allowable pressure drop is 5 psi. What diameter of tubing can be used?

SOLUTION:

Step I.   Pressure drop for 100 feet would be two times the allowable pressure drop for 50 feet, i.e., 10 psi.

Step II.   By looking at Charts I-1 to I-6, it can be determined that

APPENDIX — SECTION I

only ¾ " or 1" O.D. tubing can be used as the pressure drop would be over 10 psi for a 4 GPM flow in smaller tubing. From Chart I-5, for 4 GPM flow rate, the pressure drop per 100 feet of any of the ¾ " O.D. tubes would be satisfactory.

Step III. The smallest I.D. on Chart I-5 is 0.560. An I.D. of 0.560 on Chart I-7 shows velocity of 5 feet per second for 4 GPM. Therefore, any of the ¾ " tubing can be used and wall thickness selection would be determined by pressure requirements.

EXAMPLE 2. Suppose the maximum pressure drop of Example 1 was 1 psi. Find the proper size tubing.

SOLUTION:

Step I.   For 100 feet, maximum pressure drop would be 2 psi.

Step II.   ¾ " tubing is now too small as determined by Chart I-5. Looking at Chart I-6, it can be seen that 1" O.D. tubing of wall thickness less than 0.100 can be used because it will have less than a 2 psi pressure drop.

For liquids with specific gravity near water, the equivalent water flow rate can be calculated and then used to find pressure drop. An example follows:

Equivalent Flow Rate of water = Flow Rate of other liquid times $\sqrt{\text{S. G. Liquid}}$

$Q_W = Q_2 \sqrt{\text{specific gravity of other liquid}}$

EXAMPLE 3. Acetone at 1/10 GPM is to flow through 100 feet of tubing with a pressure drop not to exceed 5 psi.

SOLUTION:

Step I. $Q_W = Q_2 \sqrt{\text{S. G. L.}}$

$= 1/10 \sqrt{.792}$ (Specific Gravity Acetone $= .792$)

$= 0.089$ GPM Water

Step II.   Chart I-2 shows that ¼ " O.D. tubing of wall thickness 0.049 or less will be of sufficient I.D. to produce less than a 5 psi drop with a water flow of 0.089 GPM.

CHART I-1   ⅛ Inch O.D. Tubing

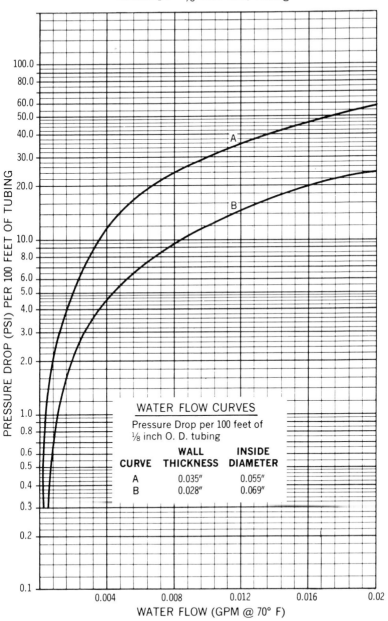

WATER FLOW CURVES
Pressure Drop per 100 feet of
⅛ inch O. D. tubing

CURVE	WALL THICKNESS	INSIDE DIAMETER
A	0.035″	0.055″
B	0.028″	0.069″

PRESSURE DROP (PSI) PER 100 FEET OF TUBING

WATER FLOW (GPM @ 70° F)

CHART I-2 ¼ Inch O.D. Tubing

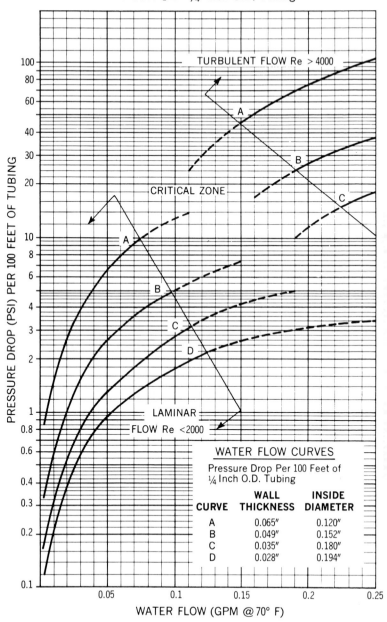

TURBULENT FLOW Re > 4000

CRITICAL ZONE

LAMINAR FLOW Re <2000

PRESSURE DROP (PSI) PER 100 FEET OF TUBING

WATER FLOW (GPM @ 70° F)

WATER FLOW CURVES

Pressure Drop Per 100 Feet of
¼ Inch O.D. Tubing

CURVE	WALL THICKNESS	INSIDE DIAMETER
A	0.065"	0.120"
B	0.049"	0.152"
C	0.035"	0.180"
D	0.028"	0.194"

CHART I-3   ⅜ Inch O.D. Tubing

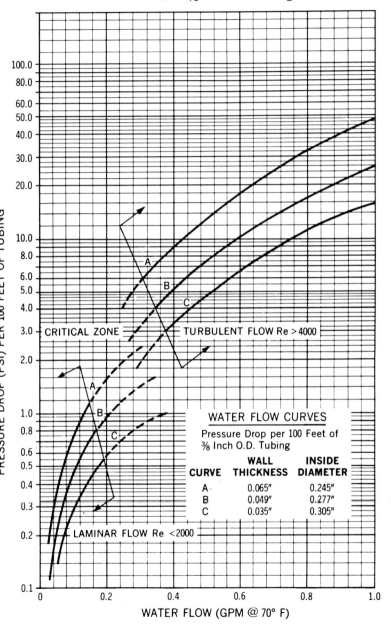

WATER FLOW CURVES

Pressure Drop per 100 Feet of
⅜ Inch O.D. Tubing

CURVE	WALL THICKNESS	INSIDE DIAMETER
A	0.065″	0.245″
B	0.049″	0.277″
C	0.035″	0.305″

PRESSURE DROP (PSI) PER 100 FEET OF TUBING

WATER FLOW (GPM @ 70° F)

CRITICAL ZONE
TURBULENT FLOW Re >4000
LAMINAR FLOW Re <2000

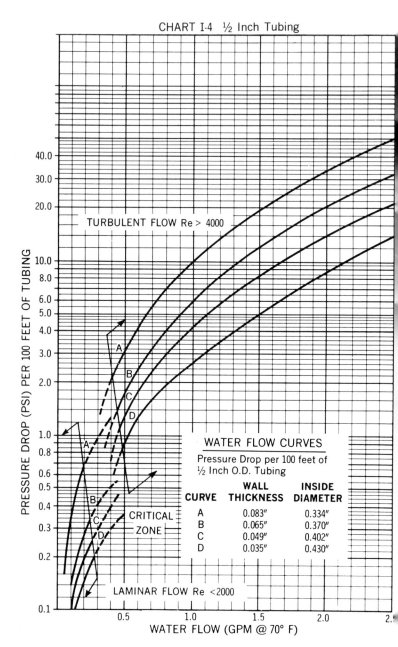

CHART I-4 ½ Inch Tubing

PRESSURE DROP (PSI) PER 100 FEET OF TUBING

WATER FLOW (GPM @ 70° F)

TURBULENT FLOW Re > 4000

CRITICAL ZONE

LAMINAR FLOW Re <2000

WATER FLOW CURVES

Pressure Drop per 100 feet of
½ Inch O.D. Tubing

CURVE	WALL THICKNESS	INSIDE DIAMETER
A	0.083″	0.334″
B	0.065″	0.370″
C	0.049″	0.402″
D	0.035″	0.430″

CHART I-5 ¾ Inch O.D. Tubing

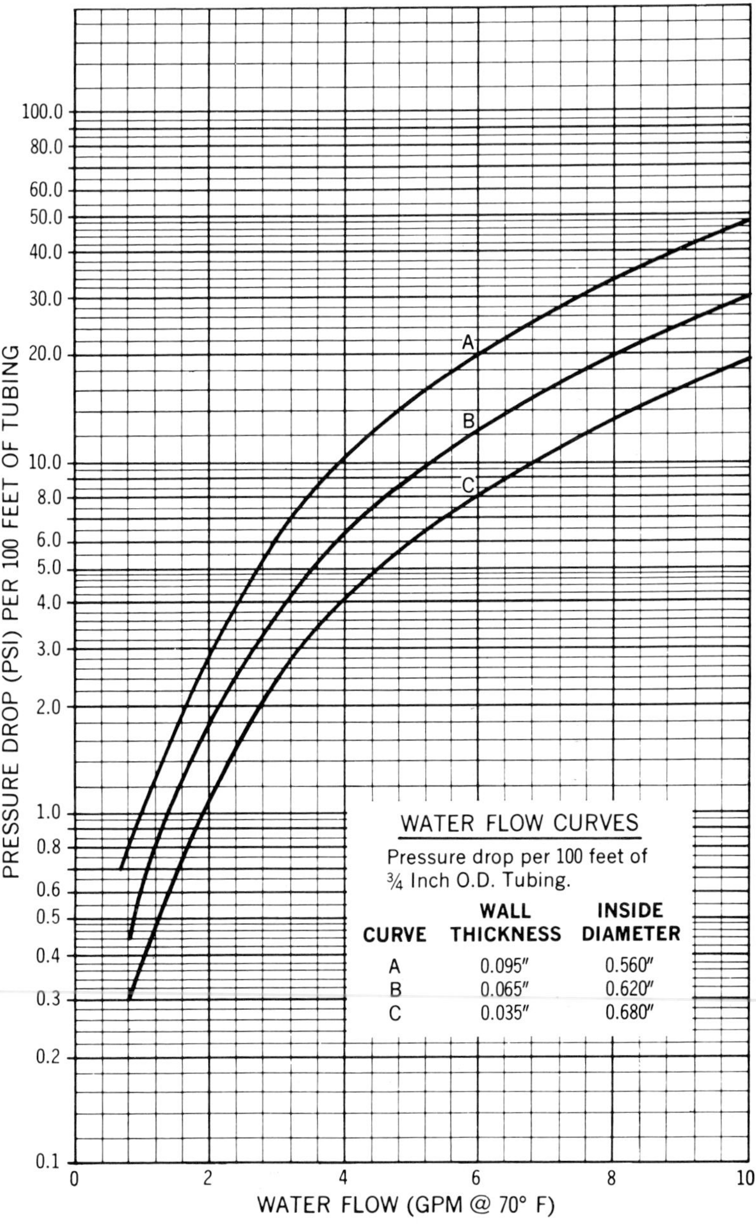

PRESSURE DROP (PSI) PER 100 FEET OF TUBING
100.0
80.0
60.0
50.0
40.0
30.0
20.0
10.0
8.0
6.0
5.0
4.0
3.0
2.0
1.0
0.8
0.6
0.5
0.4
0.3
0.2
0.1
0
2
4
6
8
10
WATER FLOW (GPM @ 70° F)
A
B
C
WATER FLOW CURVES
Pressure drop per 100 feet of ¾ Inch O.D. Tubing.
CURVE
WALL THICKNESS
INSIDE DIAMETER
A 0.095″ 0.560″
B 0.065″ 0.620″
C 0.035″ 0.680″

CHART I-6 1 Inch O.D. Tubing

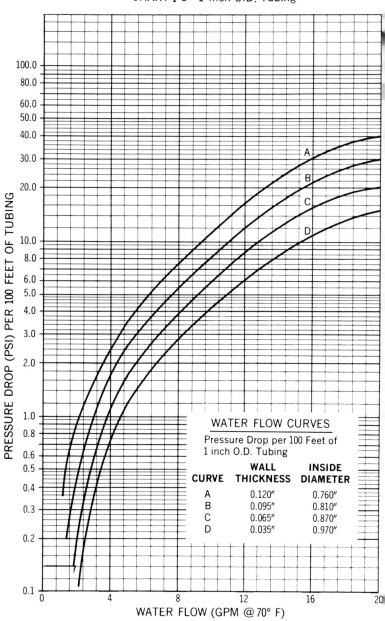

WATER FLOW (GPM @ 70° F)

PRESSURE DROP (PSI) PER 100 FEET OF TUBING

WATER FLOW CURVES

Pressure Drop per 100 Feet of
1 inch O.D. Tubing

CURVE	WALL THICKNESS	INSIDE DIAMETER
A	0.120″	0.760″
B	0.095″	0.810″
C	0.065″	0.870″
D	0.035″	0.970″

CHART I-7
MEAN VELOCITY VS TUBE INSIDE DIAMETER
FOR VARIOUS WATER FLOWS

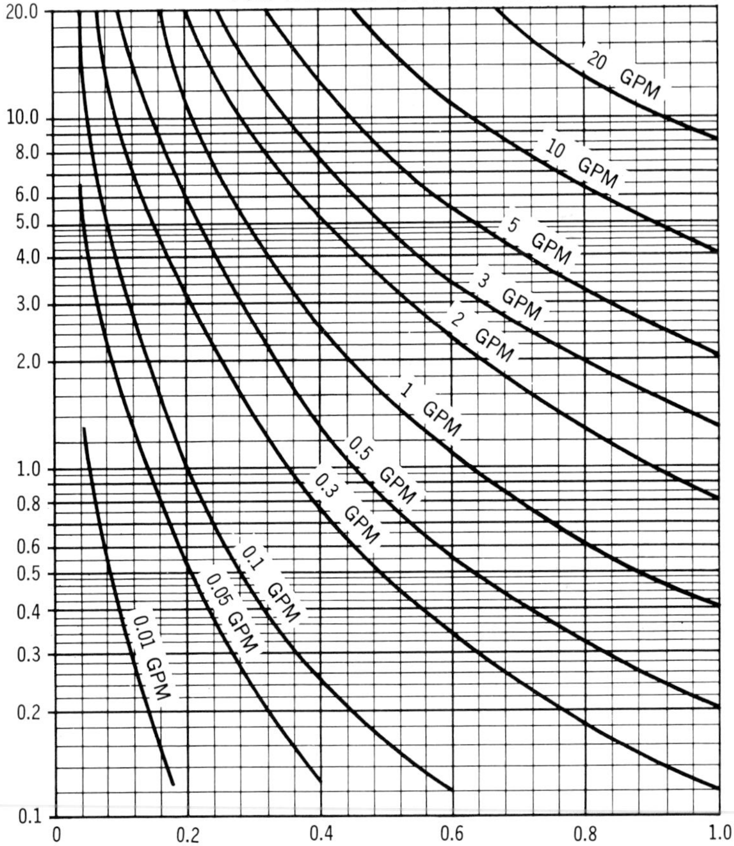

INSIDE DIAMETER (INCHES)

APPENDIX — SECTION I

CALCULATIONS FOR GAS SYSTEMS (Charts I-8 through I-14)

Pressure drop is directly proportional to length, inversely proportional to absolute pressure and directly proportional to absolute temperature. Using this information, the pressure drop formula for use with Charts I-8 through I-14 is:

$$\triangle P_L = \frac{\triangle P}{100} \quad \frac{L}{100} \left[\frac{114.7}{14.7 + P} \right] \left[\frac{460 + t}{530} \right]$$

where $\triangle P_L$ — refers to pressure drop (in psi) of air per L feet of tubing at conditions of pressure (P in psig) and temperature (t in °F.)

$\frac{\triangle P}{100}$ — refers to pressure drop at 100 psi, 70°F. for 100 feet of tubing.

In order to use Charts I-8 through I-14, it is necessary to obtain equivalent conditions at 100 psig. This is most easily explained by example problems given below.

EXAMPLE 1. What is the pressure drop for 6 CFM of 100 psig air at 70°F. for 100 feet of ¾ ″ 0.095 wall tubing?

SOLUTION: From Chart I-12 read 7.5 psi pressure drop.

EXAMPLE 2. Same problem as 1 but for 200 feet of tubing.

SOLUTION: Pressure drop is directly proportional to length. Therefore, if 7.5 psi is drop for 100 feet, $2 \times 7.5 = 15$ psi is drop for 200 feet.

EXAMPLE 3. Same problem as 1 but for 50 feet of tubing.

SOLUTION: Pressure drop is directly proportional to length. Therefore, if 7.5 psi is pressure drop for 100 feet, $½ \times 7.5 = 3.75$ psi is drop for 50 feet of tubing.

EXAMPLE 4. 10 CFM free air is to pass through 75 feet of tubing at 80 psig inlet pressure and 75°F. The diameter of the proper tubing is to be found knowing the maximum allowable pressure drop is 6 psi.

SOLUTION:

Step I. Find the pressure drop 100 feet at 70°F. and 100 psig so that the Charts may be used.

$$\triangle P = 6 = \frac{\triangle P}{100} \left(\frac{75}{100} \right) \left[\frac{114.7}{14.7 + 80} \right] \left[\frac{460 + 75}{530} \right]$$

$\frac{\triangle P}{100} = 6.55$ psi drop per 100 feet at 100 psig @ 70°F.

APPENDIX — SECTION I

Step II.   On Chart I-11 it can be noted that all ½″ tubing will
           give a pressure drop of less than 6.55 psi at 10 CFM
           free air flow.

EXAMPLE 5. Helium is to pass through 100 feet of tubing at 25 psig
inlet pressure and 70°F. The flow rate of free helium is 8 CFM. What
is the pressure drop in ⅜″, 0.035 wall tubing?

SOLUTION:

Step I.   Find the equivalent air flow so that air flow charts may
          be used.

flow rate of air = flow rate of helium $\sqrt{\text{specific gravity of helium}}$

$$Q_a = QHe \ \sqrt{(S.\,G.)\,He}$$

$$Q_a = 8 \ \sqrt{.138} = 3 \text{ CFM free air}$$

Step II.   Enter Chart I-10 and find pressure drop of 100 psig air
           at 3 CFM free air flow rate is 1.1 psi for 100 feet of
           tubing.

Step III. Solve for pressure drop in problem by using pressure
           drop formula.

$$\triangle P = \frac{P}{100} \left(\frac{L}{100}\right) \left(\frac{114.7}{14.7 + P}\right) \left(\frac{460 + t}{530}\right)$$

$$= 1.1 \left(\frac{100}{100}\right) \left(\frac{114.7}{14.7 + 25}\right) \left(\frac{530}{530}\right)$$

$$= 1.1 \,(2.9) = 3.2 \text{ psi pressure drop.}$$

EXAMPLE 6. 8 CFM of 15 psig, 70° F. air is to pass through 10 feet
of ½″ O.D., 0.049 wall tubing. What is the pressure drop?

SOLUTION:

Step I.   Change flow rate at 15 psig to flow rate at 100 psig.

$$Q_{air}@\,100 = Q_{air}@\,15 \left(\frac{14.7 + 15}{100 + 14.7}\right) = \ 8 \left(\frac{29.7}{114.7}\right) = 2.07$$

Step II.   From Chart I-11, pressure drop at 100 psig is found to
           be 6 psi for 100 feet of tubing.

APPENDIX — SECTION I

Step III.   Change this pressure drop to the condition of the problem.

$$\triangle P = \frac{\triangle P}{100} \left[\frac{L}{100}\right] \left[\frac{114.7}{14.7 + P}\right] \left[\frac{460 + t}{530}\right]$$

$$= 6 \left[\frac{10}{100}\right] \left[\frac{114.7}{14.7 + 15}\right] \left[\frac{530}{530}\right]$$

$$= 6 \times \frac{1}{10} \times 3.86 = 2.3 \text{ psi drop.}$$

OR:

Step I.   Change flow rate to that of free air.

$$Q_{air} @ 14.7 \text{ psig} = Q_{air} @ 15 \text{ psig} \left[\frac{14.7 + 15}{14.7}\right]$$

$$= 8 \times 2.02 =$$

$$= 16.16 \text{ free air.}$$

Step II.   Pressure drop at 100 psig for 100 feet of ½″ .049 wall tubing and 16.16 CFM free air flow is 6 psi.

Step III.   Same as step 3 above.

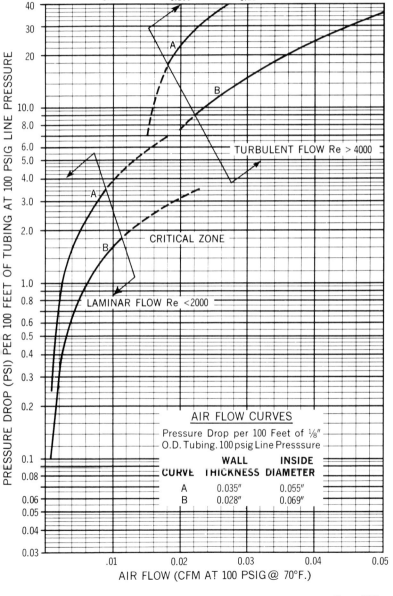

CHART I-8 ⅛" O.D. Tubing
CFM AIR STANDARD TEMPERATURE AND PRESSURE (14.7 PSIA @ 70°F.)

TURBULENT FLOW Re > 4000

CRITICAL ZONE

LAMINAR FLOW Re <2000

AIR FLOW CURVES
Pressure Drop per 100 Feet of ⅛"
O.D. Tubing. 100 psig Line Presssure

CURVE	WALL THICKNESS	INSIDE DIAMETER
A	0.035"	0.055"
B	0.028"	0.069"

PRESSURE DROP (PSI) PER 100 FEET OF TUBING AT 100 PSIG LINE PRESSURE

AIR FLOW (CFM AT 100 PSIG @ 70°F.)

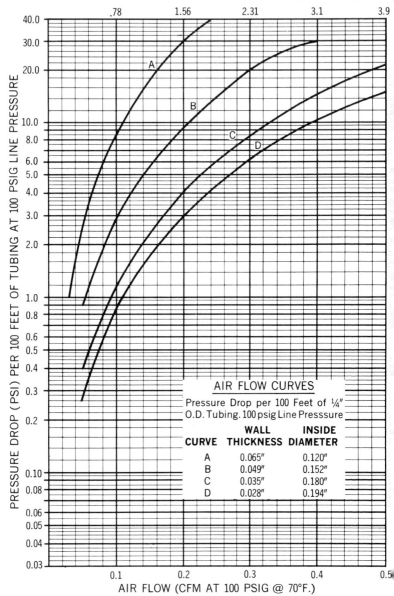

CHART I-9 — ¼" O.D. Tubing
CFM AIR STANDARD TEMPERATURE AND PRESSURE (14.7 PSIA @ 70°F.

AIR FLOW CURVES

Pressure Drop per 100 Feet of ¼"
O.D. Tubing. 100 psig Line Presssure

CURVE	WALL THICKNESS	INSIDE DIAMETER
A	0.065"	0.120"
B	0.049"	0.152"
C	0.035"	0.180"
D	0.028"	0.194"

PRESSURE DROP (PSI) PER 100 FEET OF TUBING AT 100 PSIG LINE PRESSURE

AIR FLOW (CFM AT 100 PSIG @ 70°F.)

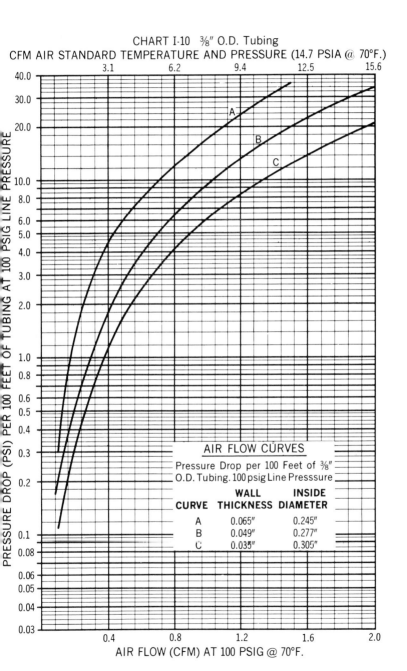

CHART I-10 ⅜" O.D. Tubing
CFM AIR STANDARD TEMPERATURE AND PRESSURE (14.7 PSIA @ 70°F.)

PRESSURE DROP (PSI) PER 100 FEET OF TUBING AT 100 PSIG LINE PRESSURE

A

B

C

AIR FLOW CURVES

Pressure Drop per 100 Feet of ⅜"
O.D. Tubing. 100 psig Line Presssure

CURVE	WALL THICKNESS	INSIDE DIAMETER
A	0.065"	0.245"
B	0.049"	0.277"
C	0.035"	0.305"

AIR FLOW (CFM) AT 100 PSIG @ 70°F.

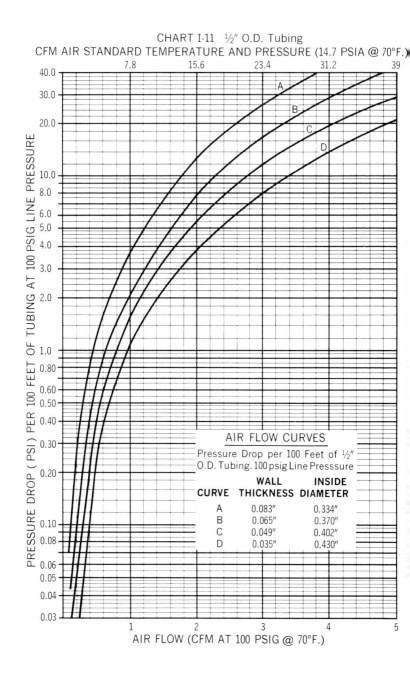

CHART I-11 ½″ O.D. Tubing

CFM AIR STANDARD TEMPERATURE AND PRESSURE (14.7 PSIA @ 70°F.)

AIR FLOW CURVES

Pressure Drop per 100 Feet of ½″
O.D. Tubing. 100 psig Line Presssure

CURVE	WALL THICKNESS	INSIDE DIAMETER
A	0.083″	0.334″
B	0.065″	0.370″
C	0.049″	0.402″
D	0.035″	0.430″

PRESSURE DROP (PSI) PER 100 FEET OF TUBING AT 100 PSIG LINE PRESSURE

AIR FLOW (CFM AT 100 PSIG @ 70°F.)

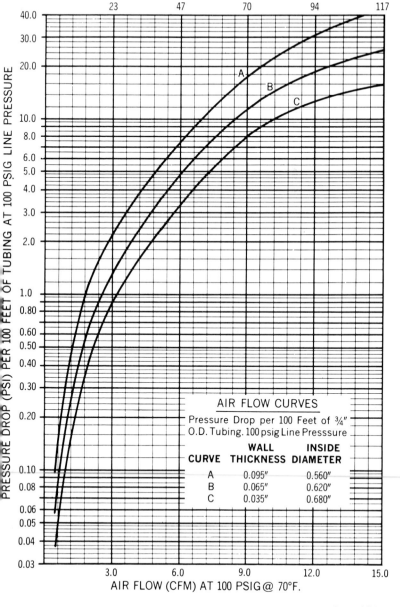

CHART I-12 ¾" O.D. Tubing

CFM AIR STANDARD TEMPERATURE AND PRESSURE (14.7 PSIA @ 70°

AIR FLOW CURVES

Pressure Drop per 100 Feet of ¾"
O.D. Tubing. 100 psig Line Presssure

CURVE	WALL THICKNESS	INSIDE DIAMETER
A	0.095″	0.560″
B	0.065″	0.620″
C	0.035″	0.680″

PRESSURE DROP (PSI) PER 100 FEET OF TUBING AT 100 PSIG LINE PRESSURE

AIR FLOW (CFM) AT 100 PSIG @ 70°F.

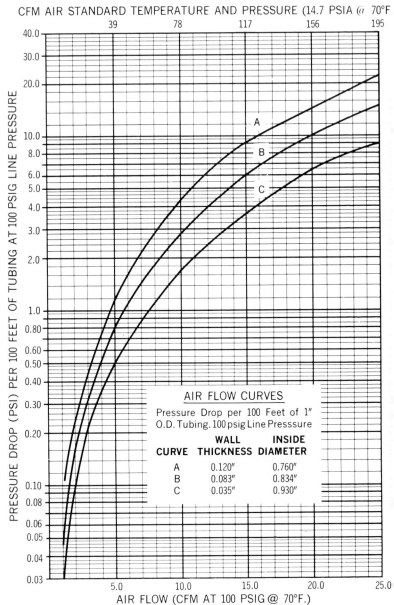

CHART I-13 1″ O.D. Tubing

CFM AIR STANDARD TEMPERATURE AND PRESSURE (14.7 PSIA @ 70°F

AIR FLOW CURVES

Pressure Drop per 100 Feet of 1″
O.D. Tubing. 100 psig Line Presssure

CURVE	WALL THICKNESS	INSIDE DIAMETER
A	0.120″	0.760″
B	0.083″	0.834″
C	0.035″	0.930″

PRESSURE DROP (PSI) PER 100 FEET OF TUBING AT 100 PSIG LINE PRESSURE

AIR FLOW (CFM AT 100 PSIG @ 70°F.)

CHART I-14

AIR VELOCITY VS TUBING I.D. FOR 100 PSIG AIR & 14.7 PSIA AIR

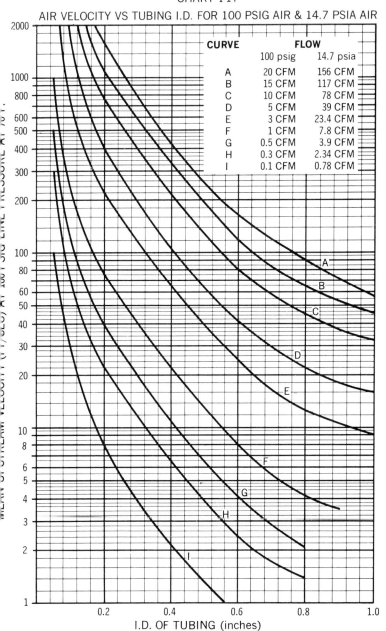

CURVE	FLOW	
	100 psig	14.7 psia
A	20 CFM	156 CFM
B	15 CFM	117 CFM
C	10 CFM	78 CFM
D	5 CFM	39 CFM
E	3 CFM	23.4 CFM
F	1 CFM	7.8 CFM
G	0.5 CFM	3.9 CFM
H	0.3 CFM	2.34 CFM
I	0.1 CFM	0.78 CFM

I.D. OF TUBING (inches)

APPENDIX

SECTION II

TUBING CALCULATIONS AND PRESSURE TABLES

Tubing I.D. and O.D. are related by the following formulas:
Tube O.D. $= 2t +$ Tube I.D.
Tube I.D. $=$ Tube O.D. $- 2t$
Where $t =$ Wall thickness in Inches.

Proper wall thickness of tubing to contain pressure may be found by using one of the SWAGELOK Allowable Pressure Charts. Pressure Tables II-1 through II-4 are for Aluminum, Copper, Carbon Steel and Type 304 and Type 316 Stainless Steel tubing, respectively.

Allowable working pressure is defined as the maximum pressure a system will encounter. Careful consideration must be given to shock loading, hazardous media, and elevated temperatures. For general service with moderate shock, a factor of 33% should be added to the system pressure. Severe shock and/or hazardous media would necessitate a factor of 50% to be added to system pressure. Table II-5 gives factors for elevated temperatures.

Some A.S.T.M. standards specify a maximum permissible variation in wall thickness of $\mp$ 10% for materials on Tables II-1 thru II-4. Therefore, values shown on these Tables should be *reduced* by 10% to take into account manufacturer's tolerances if a -10% wall thickness is allowed.

EXAMPLE 1. Air at 70°F. is to flow through soft annealed seamless copper tubing. The minimum I.D. of the tubing is .480 in. Occasional pressure surges up to 1100 psi may be encountered. What size tubing should be used?

SOLUTION:

Step I: Refer to Table II-2 for soft annealed seamless copper tubing. Since the tubing I.D. is very close to ½″, we know the smallest standard O.D. tubing we *might* be able to use is ⅝″. Locate ⅝″ in the (Tube O.D.) column of the chart and move horizontally to the right until an allowable working pressure greater than 1100 psi is found. Find 1356 psi in the fourth column over.

Step II: Reduce this value by 10% to account for manufacturing tolerances.

1356 psi
136 psi (10%)
———
1220 psi corrected allowable working pressure.

Since the corrected value is greater than 1100 psi, this size is satisfactory for 1100 psi service.

APPENDIX — SECTION II

Step III: Find the I.D. — Move vertically on the Table from 1356 psi and read .065 in. wall thickness.

Tube I.D. = Tube O.D. − 2T

Tube I.D. = .625 − 2 (.065)

Tube I.D. = .495 in.

Since this value is greater than the minimum I.D. specified, the problem is solved.

Use ⅝″ O.D. × .065 in. wall thickness Tubing. Answer.

For elevated temperatures refer to Table II-5.

PRESSURE RATINGS

This is a difficult subject to cover in simple terms, tables and graphs because of the many variables in tubing materials, wall thicknesses, hardness and surface finishes.

Although SWAGELOK Tube Fittings greatly simplfy and lower the cost of a tubing installation, certain good practices are necessary. The tubing material must be softer than the fitting material. Typical recommended ordering instructions are shown for each type of tubing.

When tubing is properly selected and handled and when SWAGELOK Tube Fittings are assembled according to instructions, assemblies will remain leak-free far beyond the allowable working pressures shown. SWAGELOK Tube Fittings have been repeatedly tested to the burst of the tubing in both the *minimum* and *maximum* wall thickness shown for each size.

SWAGELOK Tube Fittings are not normally recommended for tube wall thicknesses beyond the range shown for each size. If you have tubing thinner or thicker than shown on the tables, request information from your local distributor.

Shown in Tables II-1, II-2, II-3 and II-4 are maximum allowable working pressures for *aluminum, copper, carbon steel* and *stainless steel* tubing in various wall thicknesses.

All allowable working pressure loads are calculated from S value as specified by Table 302.3.1A and Paragraph 304.1.2 of Code for Pressure Piping ANSI B31.3.

Table II-5 shows factors for calculation of working pressures at elevated temperatures. For a given material, multiply the factor shown times allowable working pressure.

Table II-6 is a Chart of Factors. It can be used to calculate allowable pressures with other tubing materials not shown in Tables II-1, II-2, II-3 and II-4. Multiply the factor x allowable stress value in psig to determine allowable pressure.

ALLOWABLE PRESSURE CHARTS

TABLE II-1 • ALUMINUM TUBING

Minimum ultimate tensile strength 25,000 psi • For metal temperatures not to exceed −20°F. to 100°F. • Allowable working pressure loads calculated from S values as specified by Tables 302.3.1A and Paragraph 304.1.2 of Code for Pressure Piping ANSI B31.3.

Tube O.D. (In.)	Tube Wall Thickness (Inches)								SWAGELOK Fitting Series
	.035	.049	.058	.065	.083	.095	.109	.120	
3/16"	4,142	5,966	Working Pressure (PSIG)						300
1/4"	2,992	4,408	5,405						400
5/16"	2,327	3,401	4,132						500
3/8"	1,909	2,764	3,353						600
1/2"	1,406	2,014	2,422	2,755					810
5/8"	1,111	1,586	1,900	2,147					1010
3/4"		1,301	1,558	1,767	2,299				1210
7/8"		1,111	1,320	1,491					1410
1"			959	1,149	1,301	1,681	1,947		1610

SUGGESTED ORDERING INFORMATION

Aluminum-alloy drawn seamless tubing ASTM B-210 or equivalent.

TABLE II-2 • COPPER TUBING

Minimum ultimate tensile strength 30,000 psi • For metal temperatures not to exceed −20° to 100°F. • Allowable working pressure loads calculated from S values as specified by Table 302.3.1A and Paragraph 304.1.2 of Code for Pressure Piping ANSI B31.3.

Tube O.D. (In.)	Tube Wall Thickness (Inches)								SWAGELOK Fitting Series
	.028	.035	.049	.065	.083	.095	.109	.120	
1/8"	3,198	4,056	Working Pressure (PSIG)						200
3/16"	2,034	2,616	3,768						300
1/4"	1,464	1,890	2,784	3,750					400
5/16"		1,470	2,148	2,952					500
3/8"		1,206	1,746	2,412					600
1/2"		888	1,272	1,740	2,292				810
5/8"			1,002	1,356	1,776	2,076			1010
3/4"			822	1,116	1,452	1,686	1,968		1210
7/8"			702	942	1,230	1,422	1,656		1410
1"			606	822	1,062	1,230	1,428	1,590	1610

SUGGESTED ORDERING INFORMATION.

Soft annealed seamless copper tubing ASTM B-75 or equivalent.

TABLE II-3 • CARBON STEEL TUBING

Soft annealed carbon steel hydraulic tubing ASTM A-179 or equivalent • Minimum ultimate tensile strength 47,000 psi • For metal temperatures not to exceed −20° to 100°F. • Allowable working pressure loads calculated from S values as specified by Table 302.3.1A and Paragraph 304.1.2. of Code for Pressure Piping ANSI B31.3

Tube O.D. (In.)	Tube Wall Thickness (Inches)													SWAGELOK Fitting Series
	.028	.035	.049	.065	.083	.095	.109	.120	.134	.148	.165	.180	.220	
	Working Pressure (PSIG)													
1/8"	8,341	10,579												200
3/16"	5,305	6,823	9,828											300
1/4"	3,818	4,929	7,261	9,781										400
5/16"		3,834	5,602	7,699										500
3/8"		3,145	4,554	6,291										600
1/2"		2,316	3,317	4,538	5,978									810
5/8"		1,831	2,613	3,536	4,632	5,414								1010
3/4"			2,144	2,910	3,787	4,397	5,133							1210
7/8"			1,831	2,457	3,208	3,709	4,319							1410
1"			1,580	2,144	2,770	3,208	3,724	4,147						1610
1 1/4"				1,698	2,195	2,533	2,934	3,255	3,670	4,094	4,619	5,094		2000
1 1/2"					1,812	2,088	2,415	2,675	3,011	3,353	3,775	4,155	5,201	2400
2"						1,545	1,784	1,973	2,216	2,462	2,765	3,036	3,775	3200

SUGGESTED ORDERING INFORMATION

Soft annealed seamless carbon steel hydraulic tubing ASTM A-179 or equivalent. Hardness Rb 72 or less. Tubing to be free of scratches. Suitable for bending and flaring.

TABLE II-4 • STAINLESS STEEL TUBING

Annealed 304 or 316 stainless steel tubing ASTM A-269 or equivalent • Minimum ultimate tensile strength 75,000 psi • For metal temperatures not to exceed −20° to 100°F. • Allowable working pressure loads calculated from S values as specified by Table 302.3.1A and Paragraph 304.1.2 of Code for Pressure Piping ANSI B31.3

Tube O.D. (In.)	Tube Wall Thickness (Inches)																SWAGELOK Fitting Series
---	.010	.012	.014	.016	.020	.028	.035	.049	.065	.083	.095	.109	.120	.134	.156	.188	
									Working Pressure (PSIG)								
1/16"	6,880	8,510	10,240	12,075	16,125												100
1/8"						9,993	12,675										200
3/16"						6,356	8,175	11,775									300
1/4"						4,575	5,906	8,700	11,718								400
5/16"							4,593	6,712	9,225								500
3/8"							3,768	5,456	7,537								600
1/2"							2,775	3,975	5,437	7,162							810
5/8"								3,131	4,237	5,550	6,487						1010
3/4"								2,568	3,487	4,537	5,268	6,150					1210
7/8"								2,193	2,943	3,843	4,443	5,175					1410
1"								1,893	2,568	3,318	3,843	4,462	4,968				1610
1 1/4"									2,035	2,630	3,034	3,515	3,899	4,397	5,199		2000
1 1/2"										2,171	2,501	2,893	3,205	3,608	4,254	5,224	2400
2"											1,852	2,137	2,365	2,655	3,120	3,812	3200

ª For higher pressures and heavier tubing wall thickness, see High Pressure Fittings subsection of this manual, page 189.

SUGGESTED ORDERING INFORMATION

Fully annealed Type (304, 316, etc.) (seamless or welded and drawn) stainless steel hydraulic tubing ASTM A-269 or equivalent. Hardness Rb 80 or less. Tubing to be free of scratches. Suitable for bending and flaring.

APPENDIX — SECTION II

TABLE II-5 • PRESSURE RATINGS AT ELEVATED
TEMPERATURES

FACTORS					
°F.	Aluminum ASTM B-210	Copper ASTM B-75	Steel ASTM A-179	304 S.S. ASTM A-269	316 S.S. ASTM A-269
200	.87	.97	.96	.89	.99
400	.40	.45	.87	.73	.94
600	....	....	.79	.62	.92
800	....	....	.60	.53	.90
1000	....	....	.18	.47	.75
1200	....	....	....	.24	.35
1400	....	....	....	.07	.14
1600	....	....	....	....	.06
1800	....	....	....	....	.05

To determine allowable pressure at elevated temperatures, multiply allowable working pressure from Table II-1, 2, 3, or 4 by factor shown in Table 5.

EXAMPLE:

Type 316 Stainless Steel ½ " O.D. × .035" Wall at 1000°F.
2775 psi × .75 = 2081 psi

Allowable working pressure for ½ " O.D. × .035" wall type 316 stainless steel tubing is therefore 2081 psi at 1000°F.

CALCULATING BURST PRESSURES

The SWAGELOK Chart of Factors Table II-6 has been prepared, using Lame's and Boardmen's formulas, so that burst pressures, yield pressures or allowable working pressures of tubing can be calculated easily and quickly without going through the complete calculations.

EXAMPLE 1. Calculate the burst pressure of ½ " O.D. × .065" wall thickness annealed 304 Stainless Steel Tubing (ASTM A-269) at 70°F.

SOLUTION:

Step I.   Refer to specification ASTM A-269 or table 302.3 1A of Code for Pressure Piping ANSI B 31.3 and note the minimum ultimate tensile strength of the material at the given temperature. In this case the value is 75,000 psi (Table II-7).

Step II.   Locate ½ " in the (Tube O.D.) column of the SWAGELOK

Chart of Factors (Table II-6). Move horizontally to the right until the vertical column headed .065″ (wall thickness) is reached. The factor located is .290. From the top of the SWAGELOK Chart of Factors, the formula for Burst Pressure is:

Calculated Burst Pressure = Factor from table ×
    Minimum Ultimate Tensile Strength in psi.

Calculated Burst Pressure = .290 × 75,000

*Calculated Burst Pressure = 21750 × psi. Answer

*When a −10% wall thickness is allowed, this value should be reduced by 10% to take into account manufacturing tolerances.

TABLE II-6 • CHART OF FACTORS

For use in calculating Allowable Working Pressures of Tubing

Allowable working pressure = Factor × Allowable Stress Value in PSI

Allowable working pressure loads should be calculated from S values for a given metal temperature-degrees F — as specified by Table 302.3.1A and Paragraph 304.1.2 of Code for Pressure Piping ANSI B31.3

Tube O.D. (In.)	.010	.012	.014	.016	.020	.028	.035	.049	.065	.083	.095	.109	.120	.134	.148	.156	.165	.180	.188	.220	SWAGELOK Fitting Series
1/16"	.367	.454	.546	.644	.860																100
1/8"						.533*	.676*														200
3/16"						.339	.436*	.628*													300
1/4"						.244	.315	.464	.625*												400
5/16"							.245	.358	.492*												500
3/8"							.201	.291	.402*												600
1/2"							.148	.212	.290	.382											810
5/8"							.117	.167	.226	.296	.346										1010
3/4"								.137	.186	.242	.281	.328									1210
7/8"								.117	.157	.205	.237	.276									1410
1"								.101	.137	.177	.205	.238	.265								1610
1 1/4"									.1085	.1402	.1618	.1874	.2079	.2345	.2615	.2773	.2952	.3254	.3419		2000
1 1/2"										.1158	.1334	.1543	.1709	.1924	.2142	.2268	.2412	.2655	.2786	.3323	2400
2"											.0987	.1139	.1260	.1416	.1573	.1664	.1766	.1939	.2033	.2412	3200

*Lame's Formula

*For reference work only. No implication is made that these figures can be used for design work. Application codes and practices in industry should be considered. Crawford Fitting Company is not responsible for the accuracy of information presented in this table.

APPENDIX — SECTION II

TABLE II-7—STRENGTH OF TUBING MATERIALS

Tubing Material	Ultimate Tensile Strength*	Yield Strength*	ASTM No.
Aluminum (5052-0)	25,000	10,000	B-210
Copper (Soft Temper)	32,000	10,000	B-75
Carbon Steel	47,000	26,000	A-179
Hastelloy B	130,000	60,000	B-335
Hastelloy C	115,000	55,000	B-336
Inconel-600 (Annealed)	85,000	35,000	B-166
Monel-(400)	75,000	35,000	B-164
Nickel (Annealed)	60,000	20,000	B-160
Stainless Steel (304)	75,000	30,000	A-269
Stainless Steel (316)	75,000	30,000	A-269
Tantalum	50,000	27,000	B-364
Titanium (Annealed)	78,700	62,800	B-348
Zirconium (Annealed)	49,000	—	B-351

*In pounds per square inch at room temperature.

APPENDIX

SECTION III

CORROSION CHARTS

NOTE: USE THIS CORROSION CHART WITH CAUTION!

The data presented is believed reliable but a chart of this sort cannot cover all conditions of concentration, temperature, impurities and aeration. It is suggested that this chart be used only to select possible materials for use and then more extensive investigation be made of published corrosion results under the specific conditions expected. Where such information cannot be found, corrosion testing should be conducted under actual usage conditions to determine which materials can be utilized.

APPENDIX — SECTION III

	Aluminum	Brass	Steel	Monel	316 SS	TFE	Zytel	Polyethylene	Buna-N	Viton	Neoprene	Delrin
1. Excellent.												
2. Good, Most Conditions.												
3. Fair, Limited life and restricted conditions.												
4. Unsatisfactory.												
Acetaldehyde	2	4		1	1	1	3		4	3	4	2
Acetic Acid	2	4	4	1	1	1	4	3	3	4	3	4
Acetic Anhydride	1	4	4	1	1	1	2		3	4	3	4
Acetone	1	1	1	1	1	1	2	3	4	4	3	1
Acetylene	1	2	1		1	1			1	1	1	1
Acrylonitrile	2	1	1		1	1			4	3	4	4
Alcohols	2	2	2	1	1	1	2		1	1	1	1
Aluminum Chloride	4	4	4	2	4	1	2	2	2	1	2	1
Aluminum Fluoride			4		3	1	2	2				
Aluminum Hydroxide				2	1	1	2					
Aluminum Sulfate	3	4	4	1	3	1	2	2	1	1	1	1
Amines	2	2	2	1	1	1	2			4	4	1
Ammonia Anhydrous	2	4	1	1	1	1	2	2	2	3	2	
Ammonium Bicarbonate		4			1	1	2	1	2	1	1	1
Ammonium Carbonate	2	2	2		2	1			2	2	1	1
Ammonium Chloride	4	4	3	1	3	1	2	2	2	1	1	1
Ammonium Hydroxide	2	4	2	4	1	1	3	2	3	1	1	1
Ammonium Monophosphate	2	4	4		2	1	1	1	1	1	1	2
Ammonium Nitrate	3	4	1	3	1	1	2	2	1	1	1	1
Ammonium Phosphate	1		1	1	1	1			1	1	1	1
Ammonium Sulfate	2	4	3	1	2	1			1	1	1	1
Ammonium Sulfite	4	4	4	3	2	1	2					
Amyl Acetate	1		3		1	1			4	4	4	2
Aniline	4		1		1	1			4	3	3	1
Apple Juice	2	3	4		2	1			1	1	1	1
Arsenic Acid					1	1	2		1	1	1	1
Asphalt	1	2	1	1	1	1	1		3	1	3	1
Barium Carbonate	1	1	1	1	1	1	1	1	1	1	1	1
Barium Chloride	4	4	3	1	1	1	3	2	1	1	1	1
Barium Hydroxide	4	3	3	1	1	1	2	2	1	1	1	1
Barium Nitrate		4	3	3	1	1	2	2				
Barium Sulfate					1	1		2	1	1	1	1
Barium Sulfide					1	1		2	1	1	1	1
Beer	1	2	3	1	1	1	2		1	1	1	1
Beet Sugar Liquors	1	3	2	1	1	1	2		1	1	1	1
Benzene	1	1	2	1	1	1			4	2	4	1
Borax	3	3	2	1	1	1	2	2	1	1	1	1
Black Sulfate Liquor	4	2	1		1	1			2		1	
Boric Acid	2	4	4	2	2	1	2		1	1	1	1
Brine			3	1	2	1			1	1	1	1
Bromine Dry	4	2	4	1	4	1	4	2	4	2	4	
Bromine Wet	4	4	4	3	4	1		4	4	2	4	
Bunker Oil	1	2	2		1	1			1	1	2	1
Buttermilk	1	4	4	1	1	1	1	1	1	1	1	1
Butyric Acid	2	3	3	2	2	1	3	2	2	3	3	1
Calcium Bisulphite	4	4	4	4	2	1						
Calcium Carbonate	1	1	1	1	1	1	1	1	1	1	1	1
Calcium Chloride	3	3	3	1	1	1	2		1	1	1	1
Calcium Hydroxide	3	4	1	1	1	1	2		1	1	1	1
Calcium Hypochlorite	4	4	3	3	2	1			2	1	2	1
Calcium Sulphate	1				1	1	2		1	1	1	1

SEE NOTE PAGE 253

APPENDIX — SECTION III

1. Excellent.
2. Good, Most Conditions.
3. Fair, Limited life and restricted conditions.
4. Unsatisfactory.

	Aluminum	Brass	Steel	Monel	316 SS	TFE	Zytel	Polyethylene	Buna-N	Viton	Neoprene	Delrin
Carbolic Acid	2	3	3	2	1	1	2		4	2	4	4
Carbon Bisulfide	1	3	2		2	1			4	1	4	1
Carbon Dioxide	1	1	2	1	1	1	2	2	3	1	2	
Carbon Disulphide	1	3	2	2	1	1	2	4				
Carbonic Acid	2	3	4	1	1	1	2	2	1	1	1	1
Carbon Tetrachloride—Wet	4	2	3	1	1	1	2	3	4	2	4	1
Carbon Tetrachloride—Dry	2	3	2		1	1			4	2	4	1
Carbonated Water	1	2	2		1	1			1	1	1	1
Castor Oil	1	1	2		1	1			1	1	2	1
Chlorinated Solvent	4	3	3		2	1			4	3	4	1
Chloric Acid	4	4	4	3	3	1						
Chlorinated Water	4	4	4	1	3	1	4					
Chlorine Gas, Dry	2	2	2	1	2	1	4	3	3	2	3	1
Chlorine Gas, Wet	4	4	4	3	3	1	4	3	4		4	
Chloroform—Dry	4				1	1	2		4	2	4	1
Chlorosolphonic Acid—Dry	2	4	4	2	2	1	4		4		4	
Chlorosolphonic Acid—Wet	4	4	4		4	1			4		4	
Chrome Alum	3	3	2		1	1			2		2	
Chromic Acid	3	3	2	2	1	1	4	2	4	3	4	4
Citric Acid	2	4	4	2	2	1	4	4	1	1	1	1
Coconut Oil	2	2	3		2	1			1	1	2	1
Coke Oven Gas	1	3	2		1	1			2	2	3	
Copper Acetate	4	4	4		1	1						
Copper Chloride	4	4	4	2	4	1	4		1	1	1	1
Copper Nitrate	4	4	4	4	1	1	4	2	1	1	1	1
Copper Sulfate	2	2	3		3	1						
Corn Oil	4	4	4	4	1	1	4	2	1	1	1	2
Cottonseed Oil	2	2	3		2	1			1	1	2	1
Creosote	2	3	2	1	1	1		4	4	1	4	4
Crude Oil, Sweet	1	2	2		1	1			1	1	2	
Diacetone Alcohol	1	1	1		1	1			4		3	
Diesel Fuel	1	1	1		1	1			1	1	3	1
Diethylamine	1	1	1		1	1			2		3	
Dowtherm	1	1	2		1	1			4	1	4	1
Drying Oil	3	3	3		2	1			1		2	1
Epsom Salt	1	2	3		2	1			1	1	1	1
Ethane	1	1	2		2	1			1	1	2	1
Ethers	1	2	1		1	1			3	3	3	3
Ethyl Acetate	3	3	1	1	1	1			4	4	4	1
Ethyl Alcohol	2	2	2		2	1			1	1	1	1
Ethyl Chloride—Dry	1	2	1	1	1	1		4	3		3	1
Ethyl Chloride—Wet	4	3	4		2	1			3		3	1
Ethylene Glycol	2	2	1	1	1	1	2	2	1	4	1	3
Ethylene Oxide	1	1	2		2	1			4	4	4	1
Fatty Acid	1	2	2	1	1	1	2		2	1	2	1
Ferric Chloride	4	4	4	3	4	1	4	2	1	1	1	1
Ferric Nitrate	4	4	4	4	1	1		2	1	1	1	1
Ferric Sulfate	4	4	4	3	2	1	4	2	1	1	1	1
Ferrous Chloride				3	4	1	4		1	1	1	1
Ferrous Sulfate	2	4	3	1	1	1	4	2	1	1	1	1
Fish Oils	2	2	2		1	1			1	1	2	1

SEE NOTE PAGE 253

APPENDIX — SECTION III

1. Excellent. 2. Good, Most Conditions. 3. Fair, Limited life and restricted conditions. 4. Unsatisfactory.	Aluminum	Brass	Steel	Monel	316 SS	TFE	Zytel	Polyethylene	Buna-N	Viton	Neoprene	Delrin
Fluorine—Dry	2	3	3	1	2	1		2				
Fluorine—Wet	4	4	4	2	4	1		2			3	
Fluroboric Acid	1		1	1	1							
Fluorosilicic Acid	4	1	4		1	1					3	
Formaldehyde Cold	1	1	1		1	1			2		2	1
Formaldehyde Hot	2	2	4		3	1			2		2	1
Formic Acid Cold	4	2	4		2	1			4	1	1	4
Formic Acid Hot	4	2	4		2	1			4	1	1	4
Freon	2	2	3	1	3	1	2	2	3	3	3	
Fuel Oil	1	2	2		1	1			1	1	2	1
Furfural	1	3	2	2	2	1		4	4	1	3	1
Gasoline	1	1	1	1	1	1	1	4	3	1	4	1
Gas, Manufactured	2	2	2		2	1			1	1	1	1
Gas, Natural	2	2	2		1	1			1	1	1	1
Gas Odorizers	1	1	2		2	1			1	1	1	1
Gelatin	1	1	4		1	1			1	1	1	1
Glucose	1	1	2		1	1			1	1	1	1
Glue	1	2	1		2	1			1	1	1	
Glycerine	1	2	1	1	1	1	2	4	1	1	1	3
Glycols	1	2	2		2	1				1	1	3
Grease	1	2	1		1	1			1	1	2	
Heptane	1	1	2		1	1			1	1	2	
Hexane	1	2	2		2	1			1	1	3	1
Hydraulic Oil	1	2	1		1	1			1	1	2	1
Hydrobromic Acid	4	4	4	2	4	1	4		3		3	
Hydrochloric Acid	4	4	4	2	4	1	4	2	2		3	4
Hydrocyanic Acid	1	4	3		1	1					2	4
Hydrofluoric Acid	4	4	3	2	4	1	4	3			3	4
Hydrogen Gas—Cold	1	2	2		1	1					2	
Hydrogen Chloride—Dry	4	3	2	1	3	1		2				
Hydrogen Chloride—Wet	4	4	4	3	4	1						
Hydrogen Peroxide—Dilute	2	4	4	2	2	1	4	2	1	1	1	
Hydrogen Peroxide—Conc.						1			4		4	
Hydrogen Sulfide—Dry	1	2	2	1	1	1	4	2	3	1	1	1
Hydrogen Sulfide—Wet	1	4	3	2	1	1	4	2	3	1	1	1
Hydrofluosilicic Acid	4	4	4	1	3	1		2	1		1	
Illuminating Gas	1	1	1		1	1			1	1	2	
Ink	3	3	4		1	1			1	1	1	1
Iodine	4	4	4	1	2	1		3	2	1	2	1
Iodoform	3	3	2		1	1				1		1
ISO-Octane	1	1	1		1	1			1	1	3	1
Isopropyl Alcohol	2	2	2		2	1			3	1	3	1
Isopropyl Ether	1	1	1		1	1			3		3	
JP-4 Fuel	1	1	1		1	1			1	1	3	1
JP-5 Fuel	1	1	1		1	1			1	1	3	1
JP-6 Fuel	1	1	1		1	1			1	1	3	1
Kerosene	1	1	1	1	1	1		2	1	1	3	1
Ketchup	1	1	1		1	1			1	1	1	1
Ketones	1	1	1		1	1			4	4	4	1
Lactic Acid	2	4	4	2	1	1		2	3	3		4
Lard Oil	1	1	3		2	1			1	1	2	1

SEE NOTE PAGE 253

APPENDIX — SECTION III

	Aluminum	Brass	Steel	Monel	316 SS	TFE	Zytel	Polyethylene	Buna-N	Viton	Neoprene	Delrin
1. Excellent. 2. Good, Most Conditions. 3. Fair, Limited life and restricted conditions. 4. Unsatisfactory.												
Magnesium Bisulfate	2	2	2		1							
Magnesium Chloride	4	4	3	1	2	1		2	1	1	1	1
Magnesium Hydroxide	4	2	2	1	1	1		2	1	1	1	1
Magnesium Hydroxide Hot	4	4	2	1	1	1	1		2	1	1	1
Magnesium Sulfate	2	3	2	1	1	1		2	1	1	1	1
Maleic Acid	2	2	2		2				1	1	1	1
Mal c Acid	2	2	2		2	1			1	1	1	1
Mayonnaise	4	4	4		1	1			1	1	1	1
Melamine Resin	2				2	1						
Mercuric Cyanide	4	4	4		1	1						
Mercury	4	4	2	1	1	1	1	2	1	1	1	1
Metnane	1	1	2		2	1			1	1	2	1
Methyl Acetate	1	1	2		1	1			4	4	4	
Methyl Acetone	1	1	1		1	1			4	4	4	
Methyl Alcohol	2	2	2		2	1			1	2	1	1
Methyl Chloride	4	4	4	4	4	1		2	3		3	1
Methylamine	1	4	2		1	1		2	3		3	1
Methyl Ethyl Ketone	1	1	1		1	1			4	4	4	1
Methylene Chloride	4	2	4	1	2	1		3	4	3	4	
Milk	1	4	4	2	1	1		3	1	1	1	1
Mineral Oil	1	1	1	1	1	1	1	1	1	1	2	1
Molasses	1	2	2	1	1	1	2	2	1	1	1	1
Muriatic Acid	4	4	4		4	1			2	1	2	4
Mustard	2	1	2		1	1			1	1	1	1
Naphtha	1	2	2	1	1	1			3	1	4	1
Naphthalene	2	2	1		2	1			3	1	4	1
Natural Gas	1		1		1	1	1	1				
Nickel Chloride	4	4	4	2	2	1		2	1	1	1	1
Nickel Nitrate	3	4	4		2	1			1	1	1	1
Nickel Sulphate	2	3	3	1	3	1		2	1	1	1	1
Nitric Acid-10%	4	4	4		1	1			3	1	2	4
Nitric Acid-30%	4	4	4		1	1			3	1	3	4
Nitric Acid-80%	2	4	4		1	1			4	2	4	4
Nitric Acid-100%	2	4	1		1	1			4	2	4	4
Nitric Acid Anhydrous	2	4	1		1	1					4	
Nitrobenzene			1		1	1	1		4	3	4	
Nitrogen	1	1	1	1	1	1	1	1	1	1	1	1
Nitrous Acid-10%	4	4	4		2	1			3	1	1	
Nitrous Oxide	3	4	2		1	1			2		2	1
Oils, Animal	1	1	1	1	1	1			1		2	
Oleic Acid	2	2	3		2	1			1	1	3	1
Oleum	2	2	2		2	1			3	3	3	4
Olive Oil	1	2	2		1	1			1	1	2	1
Oxalic Acid	3	4	4		2	1			3	1	1	3
Oxygen	1	1	2		1	1			1	1	1	1
Ozone—Dry	1	1	1	1	1	1						
Ozone—Wet	2	2	3		1	1						
Palmitic Acid	2	2	3		2	1			2	1	2	1
Paraffin	1	1	2		1	1			1	1	2	1
Paraformaldehyde	2	2	2		2	1			2		2	2
Pentane	1	1	2		1	1			1	1	2	1

SEE NOTE PAGE 253

1. Excellent.
2. Good, Most Conditions.
3. Fair, Limited life and restricted conditions.
4. Unsatisfactory.

	Aluminum	Brass	Steel	Monel	316 SS	TFE	Zytel	Polyethylene	Buna-N	Viton	Neoprene	Delrin
Parez 607			4		4	1						
Phenol			4		4	1			4	2	4	4
Phosphoric Acid-10% Cold	4	4	4		2	1			2	1	1	4
Phosphoric Acid-10% Hot	4	4	4		4	1			2	1	1	4
Phosphoric Acid-50% Cold	4	4	4		2	1			2	1	2	4
Phosphoric Acid-50% Hot	4	4	4		4	1			2	1	2	4
Phosphoric Acid-85% Cold	4	4	2		1	1			3		2	4
Phosphoric Acid-85% Hot	4	4	3		1	1			3		2	4
Phthalic Acid	2	2	3		2	1			3	1	3	1
Phtalic Anhydride	2	2	3		2	1			3	1	3	1
Picric Acid	3	2	4		2	1			3		1	
Pine Oil	1	2	2		1	1			1	1	3	1
Pineapple Juice	1	3	3		1	1			1	1	1	1
Potassium Bisulfite	3	3	4		2	1			1	1	1	1
Potassium Bromide	3	4	3	4	1	1			1	1	1	1
Potassium Carbonate	4	2	2	1	1	1	2	2	1	1	1	1
Potassium Chlorate	2	2	2	2	1	1	2	2	1	1	1	1
Potassium Chloride	3	4	4	2	2	1	2	2	1	1	1	1
Potassium Cyanide	4	4	2	2	2	1	2	2	1	1	1	1
Potassium Dichromate	1	4	3		2	1			1	1	1	1
Potassium Diphosphate	2	2	1		1	1			1	1	1	1
Potassium Ferricyanide	1	4	3	2	1	1	2	2	1	1	1	1
Potassium Ferrocyanide	1	4	3	2	1	1	2	2	1	1	1	1
Potassium Hydroxide	4	4	3	1	1	1	3	2				
Potassium Hypochlorite	4	4	4	4	2	1						
Potassium Permanganate	1	2	2	1	1	1		2				
Potassium Sulfate	1	2	2	2	2	1	2	2	1	1	1	1
Potassium Sulfide	4	4	3	1	1	1	2	2	1			
Propane	1	1	2	1	1	1			1	1	2	1
Propyl Alcohol	2	2	2	1	1	1			1		3	
Pyrogallic Acid	2	2	4	2	2	1			1	1	1	1
Salad Oil	4	4	4	2	1	1			1	1	1	1
Salicylic Acid	2	2	4	2	2	1			1	1	1	1
Salt	2	2	3		2	1		2	1	1	1	1
Seawater	2	2	3	1	1	1	2	2	1	1	1	1
Silver Bromide	1		3	1	1	1	2	1				
Silver Chloride	4	4	4	2	4	1						
Silver Nitrate	4	4		3	1	1		2	3	1	3	1
Sodium Acetate	2	2	3	1	1	1	2	2	2	1	2	1
Sodium Aluminate						1			1	1	1	1
Sodium Bicarbonate	1		3	1	1	1	2	1	1	1	1	1
Sodium Bisulfate	3	4	4	1	2	1		1	1	1	1	1
Sodium Bisulfite	4	4	4	2	2	1		2	1	1	1	1
Sodium Borate						1						
Sodium Bromide	2	3	3	1	1	1		2	1	1	1	1
Sodium Carbonate	4	4	2	1	1	1	1	1	1	1	1	1
Sodium Chlorate						1		1	1	1	1	1
Sodium Chloride	2	2	3	1	1	1	2	2	1	1	1	1
Sodium Chromate						1			1	1	1	1
Sodium Cyanide	4	4	2	1	2	1		2	1	1	1	1
Sodium Fluoride	2	2	4	1	1	1		2	1	1	1	1
Sodium Hydroxide	4	3	2	1	1	1	2	2	2	3	2	

SEE NOTE PAGE 253

APPENDIX — SECTION III

1. Excellent. 2. Good, Most Conditions. 3. Fair, Limited life and restricted conditions. 4. Unsatisfactory.	Aluminum	Brass	Steel	Monel	316 SS	TFE	Zytel	Polyethylene	Buna-N	Viton	Neoprene	Delrin
Sodium Nitrate	1	3	2	2	1	1	2	2	3	1	1	1
Sodium Perborate	3	4	3	2	1	1			3	1	1	1
Sodium Peroxide	2	4	3	2	1	1			3	1	1	1
Sodium Phosphate	4	3	3	1	1	1			2	1	2	1
Sodium Silicate	3	2	2	2	1	1	2		1	1	1	1
Sodium Sulfate	1	2	2	1	1	1	2	2	1	1	1	1
Sodium Sulfide	4	4	2	2	1	1	2	2	1	1	1	1
Sodium Sulfite	4	4	4	2	1	1	2	2				
Sodium Thiosulfate	1	2	4	2	1	1			1	1	1	1
Soybean Oil	2	2	3		1	1			1	1	2	1
Stannic Chloride	4	3	4		4	1			1	1	1	1
Starch	1	2	3		2	1			1	1	1	1
Steam-212°F.	1	1	1	1	1	1			4	3	4	4
Stearic Acid	1	3	3		2	1			1	1	3	1
Styrene	1	1	1		1	1			4		4	
Sulphate, Black Liquor	2	3	3		2	1			3	3	1	1
Sulphate, Green Liquor	2	3	3		2	1			3	3	1	1
Sulphate, White Liquor	2	3	3		2	1			3	3	1	1
Sulphur	1	4	3		2	1			4			
Sulphur Chloride	4	4	4	1	3	1						
Sulphur Dioxide—Dry	2	2	2	2	1	1	4		3	1	3	1
Sulphur Dioxide—Wet	3	4	4	4	1	1	4					
Sulphur Molten	1	4	2	1	1	1	4	4	3		4	1
Sulphur Trioxide						1						
Sulphuric Acid (0-7%)	2	3	4		2	1			2	1	1	3
Sulphuric Acid 20%	4	3	4		4	1			3	1	2	1
Sulphuric Acid 50%	4	2	4		4	1			3	1	3	4
Sulphuric Acid 100%	4	2	2		1	1			4	2	4	4
Sulphurous Acid	3	3	4		2	1			3	1	3	3
Tannic Acid	3	2	4	1	1	1		2	1	1	2	1
Tartaric Acid	1	4	4	1	1	1		4	3	1	1	1
Tetraethyl Lead	2	2	3		2	1						1
Toluene	1	1	1	1	1	1		4	4	2	4	1
Tomato Juice	1	3	3		1	1			1	1	1	1
Transformer Oil	1	2	1		1	1			1	1	2	1
Tributyl Phosphate	1	1	1	1	1	1			3		3	
Trichloroethylene	1	1	2	1	1	1	1	4	4	2	4	1
Turpentine	1	2	2	1	1	1			3	1	4	1
Urea	2	2	3		2	1						1
Varnish	1	1	3		1	1			3		1	1
Vegetable Oil	1	4	2	2	1	1			1	1	2	1
Vinegar	3	1	1	1	1	1		2	4	4	4	
Water, Boiler Feed	3	3	2	1	1	1						
Water, Fresh	1	1	3		1	1			1	1	1	1
Water, Salt	3	3	4	1	2	1		2				
Whiskey	3	3	4	3	1	1		2	1	1	1	1
Wine	3	2	4	3	1	1		2	1	1	1	1
Xylene—Dry						1			4	2	4	1
Zinc Chloride	4	4	4	2	2	1	4	2	2	1	1	1
Zinc Hydrosulfite						1			1	1	1	1
Zinc Sulfate	3	4	4	1	1	1		2	1	1	1	1

SEE NOTE PAGE 253

APPENDIX

SECTION IV

GENERAL INFORMATION

A. Birmingham Wire Gauge Table.

B. Decimal Equivalents and Inch to MM Equivalents.

C. F° - C° Conversion Table.

D. O-Ring Dimensional Table.

E. Heads and Equivalent Pressure Conversions.

F. Volume Conversions.

G. Properties of Saturated Steam.

H. Specific Gravity of Water.

I. Specific Gravity of Liquids.

J. Specific Gravity of Gases.

K. Table of Elements.

BIRMINGHAM WIRE GAUGE TABLE

B W G	Wall Thickness Decimal Equivalent in inches
30	0.012
29	0.013
28	0.014
27	0.016
26	0.018
25	0.020
24	0.022
23	0.025
22	0.028
21	0.032
20	0.035
19	0.042
18	0.049
17	0.058
16	0.065
15	0.072
14	0.083
13	0.095
12	0.109
11	0.120
10	0.134
9	0.148
8	0.165
7	0.180
6	0.203
5	0.220
4	0.238
3	0.259
2	0.284
1	0.300

APPENDIX — SECTION IV-B

DECIMAL EQUIVALENTS

8ths	32nds	64ths	
1/8 =.125	1/32=.03125	1/64=.015625	33/64=.515625
1/4 =.250	3/32=.09375	3/64=.046875	35/64=.546875
3/8 =.375	5/32=.15625	5/64=.078125	37/64=.578125
1/2 =.500	7/32=.21875	7/64=.109375	39/64=.609375
5/8 =.625	9/32=.28125	9/64=.140625	41/64=.640625
3/4 =.750	11/32=.34375	11/64=.171875	43/64=.671875
7/8 =.875	13/32=.40625	13/64=.203125	45/64=.703125
16ths	15/32=.46875	15/64=.234375	47/64=.734375
1/16=.0625	17/32=.53125	17/64=.265625	49/64=.765625
3/16=.1875	19/32=.59375	19/64=.296875	51/64=.796875
5/16=.3125	21/32=.65625	21/64=.328125	53/64=.828125
7/16=.4375	23/32=.71875	23/64=.359375	55/64=.859375
9/16=.5625	25/32=.78125	25/64=.390625	57/64=.890625
11/16=.6875	27/32=.84375	27/64=.421875	59/64=.921875
13/16=.8125	29/32=.90625	29/64=.453125	61/64=.953125
15/16=.9375	31/32=.96875	31/64=.484375	63/64=.984375

INCHES TO MM

1/16 in. =	1.59 mm	11/16 in. = 17.46 mm	
1/8 in. =	3.17 mm	3/4 in. = 19.05 mm	
3/16 in. =	4.76 mm	13/16 in. = 20.64 mm	
1/4 in. =	6.35 mm	7/8 in. = 22.22 mm	
5/16 in. =	7.94 mm	15/16 in. = 23.81 mm	
3/8 in. =	9.52 mm	1 in. = 25.40 mm	
7/16 in. =	11.11 mm	1-1/4 in. = 31.75 mm	
1/2 in. =	12.70 mm	1-1/2 in. = 38.10 mm	
9/16 in. =	14.29 mm	2 in. = 50.80 mm	
5/8 in. =	15.87 mm		

MM TO INCH EQUIVALENT

1mm=0.039 in.	8mm=0.315 in.	15mm=0.590 in.	22mm=0.866 in.
2mm=0.079 in.	9mm=0.354 in.	16mm=0.630 in.	23mm=0.905 in.
3mm=0.118 in.	10mm=0.394 in.	17mm=0.669 in.	24mm=0.944 in.
4mm=0.157 in.	11mm=0.433 in.	18mm=0.709 in.	25mm=0.984 in.
5mm=0.197 in.	12mm=0.472 in.	19mm=0.748 in.	25.4mm=1 in.
6mm=0.236 in.	13mm=0.512 in.	20mm=0.787 in.	
7mm=0.276 in.	14mm=0.551 in.	21mm=0.827 in.	

APPENDIX — SECTION IV-C

TEMPERATURE CONVERSION FORMULAS

Degrees Fahrenheit (°F)	Degrees Celsius (Centigrade) (°C)	Absolute Degrees Rankine (°R) Degrees Kelvin (K)
°F = 1.8 (°C) + 32	$°C = \dfrac{°F - 32}{1.8}$	0°R = 0K °R = °F + 459.69
°F = °R − 459.69	°C = K − 273.16	K = °C + 273.16

APPENDIX — SECTION IV-C

CELSIUS (°C) FAHRENHEIT (°F) CONVERSION TABLE
TEMPERATURE CONVERSION TABLE

°C	°F	°C	°F	°C	°F	°C	°F
—200	—328	70	158	410	770	790	1454
—180	—292	75	167	420	788	800	1472
—160	—256	80	176	430	806	810	1490
—140	—220	85	185	440	824	820	1508
—120	—184	90	194	450	842	830	1526
—100	—148	95	203	460	860	850	1562
— 95	—139	100	212	470	878	900	1652
— 90	—130	110	230	480	896	950	1742
— 85	—121	120	248	490	914	1000	1832
— 80	—112	130	266	500	932	1050	1922
— 75	—103	140	284	510	950	1100	2012
— 70	— 94	150	302	520	968	1150	2102
— 65	— 85	160	320	530	986	1200	2192
— 60	— 76	170	338	540	1004	1250	2282
— 55	— 67	180	356	550	1022	1300	2372
— 50	— 58	190	374	560	1040	1350	2462
— 45	— 49	200	392	570	1058	1400	2552
— 40	— 40	210	410	580	1076	1450	2642
— 35	— 31	212	414	590	1094	1500	2732
— 30	— 22	220	428	600	1112	1550	2822
— 25	— 13	230	446	610	1130	1600	2912
— 20	— 4	240	464	620	1148	1650	3002
— 15	5	250	482	630	1166	1700	3092
— 10	14	260	500	640	1184	1750	3182
— 5	23	270	518	650	1202	1800	3272
0	32	280	536	660	1220	1850	3362
5	41	290	554	670	1238	1900	3452
10	50	300	572	680	1256	1950	3542
15	59	310	590	690	1274	2000	3632
20	68	320	608	700	1292	2050	3722
25	77	330	626	710	1310	2100	3812
30	86	340	644	720	1328	2150	3902
35	95	350	662	730	1346	2200	3992
40	104	360	680	740	1364	2250	4082
45	113	370	698	750	1382	2300	4172
50	122	380	716	760	1400	2350	4262
55	131	390	734	770	1418	2400	4352
60	140	400	752	780	1436	2450	4442
65	149						

APPENDIX — SECTION IV-D

O-RING DIMENSIONAL TABLE

Uniform Size Number	Nominal Size (Inches) I.D. x O.D. x Cross Section	Actual Dimensions		
		I.D. (Inches)	Cross Section (Inches)	O.D. (Inches)
006	1/8 x 1/4 x 1/16	.114	.070	.254
007	5/32 x 9/32 x 1/16	.145	.070	.285
008	3/16 x 5/16 x 1/16	.176	.070	.316
009	7/32 x 11/32 x 1/16	.208	.070	.348
010	1/4 x 3/8 x 1/16	.239	.070	.379
011	5/16 x 7/16 x 1/16	.301	.070	.441
012	3/8 x 1/2 x 1/16	.364	.070	.504
013	7/16 x 9/16 x 1/16	.426	.070	.566
014	1/2 x 5/8 x 1/16	.489	.070	.629
111	7/16 x 5/8 x 3/32	.424	.103	.630
112	1/2 x 11/16 x 3/32	.487	.103	.693
113	9/16 x 3/4 x 3/32	.549	.103	.755
114	5/8 x 13/16 x 3/32	.612	.103	.818
115	11/16 x 7/8 x 3/32	.674	.103	.880
116	3/4 x 15/16 x 3/32	.737	.103	.943
117	13/16 x 1 x 3/32	.799	.103	1.005
118	7/8 x 1-1/16 x 3/32	.862	.103	1.068
119	15/16 x 1-1/8 x 3/32	.924	.103	1.130
120	1 x 1-3/16 x 3/32	.987	.103	1.193
121	1-1/16 x 1-1/4 x 3/32	1.049	.103	1.255
122	1-1/8 x 1-5/16 x 3/32	1.112	.103	1.318
123	1-3/16 x 1-3/8 x 3/32	1.174	.103	1.380
125	1-5/16 x 1-1/2 x 3/32	1.299	.103	1.505
126	1-3/8 x 1-9/16 x 3/32	1.362	.103	1.568
128	1-1/2 x 1-11/16 x 3/32	1.487	.103	1.693
130	1-5/8 x 1-13/16 x 3/32	1.612	.103	1.818
132	1-3/4 x 1-15/16 x 3/32	1.737	.103	1.943
133	1-13/16 x 2 x 3/32	1.799	.103	2.005
134	1-7/8 x 2-1/16 x 3/32	1.862	.103	2.068
136	2 x 2-3/16 x 3/32	1.987	.103	2.193
212	7/8 x 1-1/8 x 1/8	.859	.139	1.137
215	1-1/16 x 1-5/16 x 1/8	1.046	.139	1.324
219	1-5/16 x 1-9/16 x 1/8	1.296	.139	1.5/4
223	1-5/8 x 1-7/8 x 1/8	1.609	.139	1.887
902	—	.239	.064	.367
902½	—	.070	.040	.150
916	—	1.171	.116	1.403
920	—	1.475	.118	1.711
924	—	1.720	.118	1.956
932	—	2.337	.118	2.573

APPENDIX — SECTION IV-E

HEADS AND EQUIVALENT PRESSURE CONVERSIONS

TO CONVERT	INTO	MULTIPLY BY
Atmospheres	Pounds Per Sq. In.	14.696
Atmospheres	Pounds Per Sq. Ft.	2116.22
Atmospheres	In. of Water at 60°F.	407.17
Atmospheres	Ft. of Water at 60°F.	33.931
Atmospheres	In. of Mercury at 32°F.	29.921
Atmospheres	mm of Mercury at 32°F.	760
Ft. of Water at 60°F.	Pounds Per Sq. In.	0.4335
Ft. of Water at 60°F.	Pounds Per Sq. Ft.	62.43
Ft. of Water at 60°F.	In. of Water at 60°F.	12
Ft. of Water at 60°F.	In. of Mercury at 32°F.	0.8826
Ft. of Water at 60°F.	mm of Mercury at 32°F.	22.418
Ft. of Water at 60°F.	Atmospheres	0.029481
In. of Mercury at 32°F.	Pounds Per Sq. In.	0.49116
In. of Mercury at 32°F.	Pounds Per Sq. Ft.	70.7266
In. of Mercury at 32°F.	In. of Water at 60°F.	13.608
In. of Mercury at 32°F.	Ft. of Water at 60°F.	1.1340
In. of Mercury at 32°F.	mm of Mercury at 32°F.	25.40005
In. of Mercury at 32°F.	Atmospheres	0.033421
In. of Water at 60°F.	Pounds Per Sq. In.	0.03613
In. of Water at 60°F.	Pounds Per Sq. Ft.	5.204
In. of Water at 60°F.	Ft. of Water at 60°F.	0.08333
In. of Water at 60°F.	In. of Mercury at 32°F.	0.073483
In. of Water at 60°F.	mm of Mercury at 32°F.	1.8665
In. of Water at 60°F.	Atmospheres	2.458×10^{-3}

APPENDIX — SECTION IV-E

HEADS AND EQUIVALENT PRESSURE CONVERSIONS
(Continued)

TO CONVERT	INTO	MULTIPLY BY
Pounds Per Sq. Ft.	Pounds Per Sq. In.	6.9445×10^{-3}
Pounds Per Sq. Ft.	In. of Water at 60°F.	0.19224
Pounds Per Sq. Ft.	Ft. of Water at 60°F.	0.01603
Pounds Per Sq. Ft.	In. of Mercury at 32°F.	0.01414
Pounds Per Sq. Ft.	mm of Mercury at 32°F.	0.35916
Pounds Per Sq. Ft.	Atmospheres	4.725×10^{-4}
Pounds Per Sq. In.	Pounds Per Sq. Ft.	144.0
Pounds Per Sq. In.	In. of Water at 60°F.	27.684
Pounds Per Sq. In.	Ft. of Water at 60°F.	2.307
Pounds Per Sq. In.	In. of Mercury at 32°F.	2.03601
Pounds Per Sq. In.	mm of Mercury at 32°F.	51.7148
Pounds Per Sq. In.	Atmospheres	0.06804
mm of Mercury at 32°F.	Pounds Per Sq. In.	0.019337
mm of Mercury at 32°F.	Pounds Per Sq. Ft.	2.78450
mm of Mercury at 32°F.	In. of Water at 60°F.	0.53576
mm of Mercury at 32°F.	Ft. of Water at 60°F.	0.04461
mm of Mercury at 32°F.	In. of Mercury at 32°F.	0.03937
mm of Mercury at 32°F.	Atmospheres	1.3158×10^{-3}

APPENDIX — SECTION IV-F

VOLUME CONVERSION

TO CONVERT	INTO	MULTIPLY BY
Cubic Feet	Cubic Centimeters	2.83×10^4
Cubic Feet	Cubic Millimeters	0.02832
Cubic Feet	Cubic Yards	0.03704
Cubic Feet	Cubic Inches	1728
Cubic Feet	Gallons (Br.)	6.229
Cubic Feet	Liters	28.32
Cubic Feet	BBL (Oil)	0.1781
Cubic Feet	BBL (Liq.)	0.2375
Gallons	Cubic Centimeters	3785
Gallons	Cubic Millimeters	0.00379
Gallons	Cubic Feet	0.1337
Gallons	Cubic Inches	231
Gallons	Gallons (Br.)	0.8327
Gallons	Liters	3.785
Gallons	Pounds of Water	8.35
Gallons	BBL (Oil)	0.02381
Gallons	BBL (Liq.)	0.03175
Liters	Cubic Centimeters	1000
Liters	Cubic Millimeters	0.001
Liters	Cubic Yards	0.00131
Liters	Cubic Feet	0.0353
Liters	Cubic Inches	61.02
Liters	Gallons (Br.)	0.2200
Liters	Gallons	0.2642
Liters	BBL (Oil)	0.00629
Liters	BBL (Liq.)	0.00839
Cubic Centimeters	Cubic Meters	1×10^{-6}
Cubic Centimeters	Cubic Feet	3.531×10^{-5}
Cubic Centimeters	Cubic Inches	0.06102
Cubic Centimeters	Gallons (Br.)	2.20×10^{-4}
Cubic Centimeters	Gallons	2.642×10^{-4}
Cubic Centimeters	Liters	1.01×10^{-3}
Cubic Centimeters	BBL (Oil)	6.29×10^{-6}
Cubic Centimeters	BBL (Liq.)	8.39×10^{-6}

APPENDIX — SECTION IV-F

AREA

from \ to	cm²	m²	km²	in.²	ft²	mile²
cm²	1	0.0001	1×10^{10}	0.1550	0.00108	3.86×10^{11}
m²	1×10^4	1	1×10^6	1550	10.76	3.86×10^7
km²	1×10^{10}	1×10^6	1	1.55×10^9	1.08×10^7	0.3861
in.²	6.452	6.45×10^4	6.45×10^{10}	1	0.00694	2.49×10^{10}
ft²	929.0	0.09290	9.29×10^8	144	1	3.59×10^8
mile²	2.59×10^{10}	2.59×10^6	2.590	4.01×10^9	2.79×10^7	1

PRESSURE

from \ to	mm Hg	in. Hg	in. H_2	ft H_2O	atm	lb/in.²	kg/cm²
mm Hg	1	0.03937	0.5353	0.04460	0.00132	0.01934	0.00136
in. Hg	25.40	1	13.60	1.133	0.03342	0.4912	0.03453
in. H_2O	1.868	0.07355	1	0.08333	0.00246	0.03613	0.00254
ft. H_2O	22.42	0.8826	12	1	0.02950	0.4335	0.03048
atm	760	29.92	406.8	33.90	1	14.70	1.033
lb./in.²	51.71	2.036	27.67	2.307	0.06805	1	0.07031
kg/cm²	735.6	28.96	393.7	32.81	0.9678	14.22	1

1 Bar = 1×10^6 dynes/cm² = 0.98692 atm

FLOW RATE

from \ to	lit/sec	gal/min	ft³/sec	ft³/min	bbl/hr	bbl/day
lit/sec	1	15.85	0.03532	2.119	22.66	543.8
gal/min	0.06309	1	0.00223	0.1337	1.429	34.30
ft³/sec	28.32	448.8	1	60	641.1	1.54×10^4
ft³/min	0.4719	7.481	0.01667	1	10.69	256.5
bbl/hr	0.04415	0.6997	0.00156	0.09359	1	24
bbl/day	0.00184	0.02917	6.50×10^5	0.00390	0.04167	1

bbl refers to bbl oil = 42 gallons

PROPERTIES OF SATURATED STEAM

Abs press., psi	Temp., deg. F	Abs press., psi	Temp., deg. F	Abs press., psi	Temp., deg. F	Abs press., psi	Temp., deg. F	Abs press., psi	Temp., deg. F
1.0	101.74	39	265.72	85	316.25	162	364.53	540	475.01
1.2	107.92	40	267.25	86	317.07	164	365.51	560	478.85
1.4	113.26	41	268.74	87	317.88	166	366.48	580	482.58
1.6	117.99	42	270.21	88	318.68	168	367.45	600	486.21
1.8	122.23	43	271.64	89	319.48	170	368.41	620	489.75
2.0	126.08	44	273.05	90	320.27	172	369.35	640	493.21
2.2	129.62	45	274.44	91	321.06	174	370.29	660	496.58
2.4	132.89	46	275.80	92	321.83	176	371.22	680	499.88
2.6	135.94	47	277.13	93	322.60	178	372.14	700	503.10
2.8	138.79	48	278.45	94	323.36	180	373.06	720	506.25
3.0	141.48	49	279.74	95	324.12	182	373.96	740	509.34
4.0	152.97	50	281.01	96	324.87	184	374.86	760	512.36
5.0	162.24	51	282.26	97	325.61	186	375.75	780	515.33
6.0	170.06	52	283.49	98	326.35	188	376.64	800	518.23
7.0	176.85	53	284.70	99	327.08	190	377.51	820	521.08
8.0	182.86	54	285.90	100	327.81	192	378.38	840	523.88
9.0	188.28	55	287.07	102	329.25	194	379.24	860	526.63
10	193.21	56	288.23	104	330.66	196	380.10	880	529.33
11	197.75	57	289.37	106	332.05	198	380.95	900	531.98
12	201.96	58	290.50	108	333.42	200	381.79	920	534.59
13	205.88	59	291.61	110	334.77	205	383.86	940	537.16
14	209.56	60	292.71	112	336.11	210	385.90	960	539.68
14.696	212.00	61	293.79	114	337.42	215	387.89	980	542.17
15	213.03	62	294.85	116	338.72	220	389.86	1,000	544.61
16	216.32	63	295.90	118	339.99	225	391.79	1,050	550.57
17	219.44	64	296.94	120	341.25	230	393.68	1,100	556.31
18	222.41	65	297.97	122	342.50	235	395.54	1,150	561.86
19	225.24	66	298.99	124	343.72	240	397.37	1,200	567.22
20	227.96	67	299.99	126	344.94	245	399.18	1,250	572.42
21	230.57	68	300.98	128	346.13	250	400.95	1,300	577.46
22	233.07	69	301.96	130	347.32	260	404.42	1,350	582.35
23	235.49	70	302.92	132	348.48	270	407.78	1,400	587.10
24	237.82	71	303.88	134	349.64	280	411.05	1,450	591.71
25	240.07	72	304.83	136	350.78	290	414.23	1,500	596.23
26	242.25	73	305.76	138	351.91	300	417.33	1,600	604.90
27	244.36	74	306.68	140	353.02	320	423.29	1,700	613.15
28	246.41	75	307.60	142	354.12	340	428.97	1,800	621.03
29	248.40	76	308.50	144	355.21	360	434.40	1,900	628.58
30	250.33	77	309.40	146	356.29	380	439.60	2,000	635.82
31	252.22	78	310.29	148	357.36	400	444.59	2,200	649.46
32	254.05	79	311.16	150	358.42	420	449.39	2,400	662.12
33	255.84	80	312.03	152	359.46	440	454.02	2,600	673.94
34	257.08	81	312.89	154	360.49	460	458.50	2,800	684.99
35	259.28	82	313.74	156	361.52	480	462.82	3,000	695.36
36	260.95	83	314.59	158	362.03	500	467.01	3,200	705.11
37	262.57	84	315.42	160	363.53	520	471.07	3,206.2	705.40
38	264.16								

NOTE: To convert PSIA into PSIG subtract 14.7 (approx.)

SPECIFIC GRAVITY OF WATER
Versus Temperature

Water Temperature °F	Specific Gravity
32	1.0013
40	1.0013
50	1.0006
60	1.0000
70	.9989
80	.9976
90	.9963
100	.9945
110	.9920
120	.9902
130	.9872
140	.9848
150	.9817
160	.9787
170	.9751
180	.9716
190	.9681
200	.9645
210	.9605
212	.9594
220	.9565
240	.9480
260	.9386
280	.9294
300	.9193
350	.8917
400	.8606
450	.8269
500	.7863
550	.7358
600	.6797

SPECIFIC GRAVITY OF LIQUIDS

Liquid	Specific Gravity Relative to Water at 60°F.
Acetone	.792
Alcohol, Ethyl (100%)	.789
Alcohol, Methyl (100%)	.796
Acid, Muriatic (40%)	1.20
Acid, Nitric (91%)	1.50
Acid, Sulfuric (87%)	1.80
Bunkers C Fuel Max.	1.014
Distillate	.850
Fuel 3 Max.	.898
Fuel 5 Min.	.966
Fuel 5 Max.	.993
Fuel 6 Min.	.993
Gasoline	.751
Gasoline, Natural	.680
Hydrochloric Acid	1.256
Kerosene	.815
M. C. Residuum	.935
Mercury	13.570
Olive Oil	.919
Pentane	.624
SAE 10 Lube*	.876
SAE 30 Lube*	.898
SAE 70 Lube*	.916
Salt Creek Crude	.843
Sea Water	1.025
32.6° API Crude	.862
35.6° API Crude	.847
40° API Crude	.825
48° API Crude	.788
Water	1.000

*100 Viscosity Index.

SPECIFIC GRAVITY OF GASES RELATIVE TO AIR @ 70°F.

Name of Gas	Chemical Formula	Specific Gravity Relative To Air
Acetylene	C_2H_2	.9107
Air	—	1.000
Ammonia	NH_3	.5961
Anthracite Producer Gas	—	.85
Argon	A	1.377
Benzene	C_6H_6	2.6920
Bituminous Producer Gas	—	.86
Blast-Furnace Gas	—	1.000
Blue Water Gas	—	.53
Butane	C_4H_{10}	2.06654
Butylene	C_4H_8	1.9936
Carbon Dioxide	CO_2	1.5282
Carbon Monoxide	CO	.9672
Carbureted Water Gas	—	.65
Chlorine	CL_2	2.486
Coke Oven Gas	—	.42
Ethane	C_2H_6	1.04882
Ethyl Chloride	C_2H_5CL	2.365
Ethylene	C_2H_4	.974
Freon (F-12)	CCL_2F_2	4.520
Helium	He	.138
Hydrogen	H_2	.06959
Hydrogen Chloride	HCL	1.268
Hydrogen Sulphide	H_2S	1.190
Methane	CH_4	.5543
Methyl Chloride	CH_3CL	1.738
Natural Gas*	—	.667
Neon	Ne	0.696
Nitrogen	N_2	.9718
Nitric Oxide	NO	1.034
Nitrous Oxide	N_2O	1.518
Oxygen	O_2	1.1053
Pentane	C_5H_{12}	2.4872
Propane	C_3H_8	1.5617
Propylene	C_3H_6	1.4504
Sulphur Dioxide	SO_2	2.264
Toluene	C_7H_8	3.1760
Xylene	C_8H_{10}	3.6618

*Representative value

TABLE OF THE ELEMENTS

name	sym.	at. no.	at. wt.	name	sym.	at. no.	at. wt.
Actinium	Ac	89	227	Mercury	Hg	80	200.59
Aluminum	Al	13	26.9815	Molybdenum	Mo	42	95.94
Americium	Am	95	243	Neodymium	Nd	60	144.24
Antimony	Sb	51	121.75	Neon	Ne	10	20.183
Argon	Ar	18	39.948	Neptunium	Np	93	237
Arsenic	As	33	74.9216	Nickel	Ni	28	58.71
Astatine	At	85	210	Niobium	Nb	41	92.906
Barium	Ba	56	137.34	Nitrogen	N	7	14.0067
Berkelium	Bk	97	247	Nobelium	No	102	254
Beryllium	Be	4	9.0122	Osmium	Os	76	190.2
Bismuth	Bi	83	208.980	Oxygen	O	8	15.9994
Boron	B	5	10.811	Palladium	Pd	46	106.4
Bromine	Br	35	79.909	Phosphorus	P	15	30.9738
Cadmium	Cd	48	112.40	Platinum	Pt	78	195.09
Calcium	Ca	20	40.08	Plutonium	Pu	94	242
Californium	Cf	98	249	Polonium	Po	84	210
Carbon	C	6	12.01115	Potassium	K	19	39.102
Cerium	Ce	58	140.12	Praseodymium	Pr	59	140.907
Cesium	Cs	55	132.905	Promethium	Pm	61	147
Chlorine	Cl	17	35.453	Protactinium	Pa	91	231
Chromium	Cr	24	51.996	Radium	Ra	88	226
Cobalt	Co	27	58.9332	Radon	Rn	86	222
Copper	Cu	29	63.54	Rhenium	Re	75	186.2
Curium	Cm	96	247	Rhodium	Rh	45	102.905
Dysprosium	Dy	66	162.50	Rubidium	Rb	37	85.47
Einsteinium	Es	99	254	Ruthenium	Ru	44	101.07
Erbium	Er	68	167.26	Samarium	Sm	62	150.35
Europium	Eu	63	151.96	Scandium	Sc	21	44.956
Fermium	Fm	100	253	Selenium	Se	34	78.96
Fluorine	F	9	18.9984	Silicon	Si	14	28.086
Francium	Fr	87	223	Silver	Ag	47	107.870
Gadolinium	Gd	64	157.25	Sodium	Na	11	22.9898
Gallium	Ga	31	69.72	Strontium	Sr	38	87.62
Germanium	Ge	32	72.59	Sulfur	S	16	32.064
Gold	Au	79	196.967	Tantalum	Ta	73	180.948
Hafnium	Hf	72	178.49	Technetium	Tc	43	99
Helium	He	2	4.0026	Tellurium	Te	52	127.60
Holmium	Ho	67	164.930	Terbium	Tb	65	158.924
Hydrogen	H	1	1.00797	Thallium	Tl	81	204.37
Indium	In	49	114.82	Thorium	Th	90	232.038
Iodine	I	53	126.9044	Thulium	Tm	69	168.934
Iridium	Ir	77	192.2	Tin	Sn	50	118.69
Iron	Fe	26	55.847	Titanium	Ti	22	47.90
Krypton	Kr	36	83.80	Tungsten	W	74	183.85
Lanthanum	La	57	138.91	Uranium	U	92	238.03
Lawrencium	Lw	103	257	Vanadium	V	23	50.942
Lead	Pb	82	207.19	Xenon	Xe	54	131.30
Lithium	Li	3	6.939	Ytterbium	Yb	70	173.04
Lutetium	Lu	71	174.97	Yttrium	Y	39	88.905
Magnesium	Mg	12	24.312	Zinc	Zn	30	65.37
Manganese	Mn	25	54.9380	Zirconium	Zr	40	91.22
Mendelevium	Md	101	256				

APPENDIX — SECTION V

TRADEMARKS & CREDITS

VITON, TEFLON, DELRIN — T.M. E. I. duPont de Nemours and Company

INCONEL, INCONEL X, INCONEL 600, MONEL, "K" MONEL, MONEL 400, MONEL 403 —
T.M. The International Nickel Company, Inc.

HASTELLOY/ALLOY B, HASTELLOY/ALLOY C-276, HASTELLOY/ALLOY X, HAYNES #25 — T.M. Cabot Corporation

CARPENTER 20 Cb3, CARPENTER 455 —
T.M. Carpenter Technology Corporation

17-4-PH — T.M. Armco Steel Corporation

KEL-F — T.M. Minnesota Mining & Manufacturing Co.

TYGON — T.M. Norton Company

DOWTHERM A, DOWTHERM E — T.M. Dow Chemical Co.

PYREX — T.M. Corning Glass Works

SWAGELOK, FERRULE-PAK, SILVER GOOP, BLUE GOOP, HIGH PURITY GOOP, VAC GOOP, GOOP, STRIP TEEZE —
T.M. Crawford Fitting Company

CAJON, VCO, VCR, ULTRA-TORR — T.M. Cajon Company

NUPRO, SNOOP, REAL COOL SNOOP — T.M. Nupro Company

WHITEY — T.M. Whitey Research Tool Co.

SNO-TRIK — T.M. Sno-Trik Company

SOUTHWEST INDUSTRIES — Tubing application photo, page 26, Fig. 29

COMMERCIAL STRAIGHT THREAD TUBE FITTING BOSSES (page 74) Reprinted with permission, "Copyright © Society of Automotive Engineers, Inc., 1974, All rights reserved."

PIPE FITTINGS (pages 166, 167, 168, 169 and 170) — reprinted by permission of Domestic Engineering from article titled: "Industry expert calls for more care in making pipe threads". Article appeared in the October, 1961 issue.